By Legacies

an anthology by writers for writers

Editors
JAIME DILL & LIZZIE THORNTON

Cardigan Press

Cardigan Press
P.O. Box 173
Spindale, NC 28160 USA
www.cardigan.press

Cardigan Press paperback edition September 2021
Published in the United States of America

Cover concept and design by Lizzie Thornton & Jaime Dill
Cover artwork by Jaime Dill
Interior design by Lizzie Thornton & Jaime Dill

Print ISBN: 978-1-7349623-2-1

This book was bound by the faith and acceptance of the #writingcommunity of Twitter; we couldn't have done it without you.

To every person who has ever felt a spark of creativity, may these words be the catalyst for you to finally take the leap and WRITE.

Contents

Contents

A note from the editors

Hey you—ghost writers, coffee-shop writers, tea house writers, and writers reading Charlotte's Web—THANK YOU for using your precious birthday money to purchase this book. Or perhaps, it is a stolen thing—because let's face it, Twenty Twenty was tough—in which case, please leave us a great review and we'll call it even.

This is the first time after writer's block that I've actually sat down to write this letter, but I've thought about it countless times since its conception in August. I've thought about what I could possibly say during my performance to encapsulate what this book means to me, what this press means to me. And every time I would come up with a really great line, or maybe even two . . . I would fail to write it down—a youthful regret on my part; what a writer thing to do.

Regardless, today I will write. But the fact of the matter is, it doesn't matter which words I pluck from the thesaurus or which words I weave together for you because sometimes, words fail. As a writer, that isn't something I should readily admit. But it's the truth. Sometimes, one person's words aren't enough to explain a feeling that sits in the depth of your soul, that nudges you forward to take chances even though you're terrified, that moves you to tears without warning, that keeps you awake late into the crinkled nights, cultivating ideas for a future that's so close you can almost touch it, and you know if you just keep going, if you keep choosing success, one day it will all be worth it.

Without social media, *without Twitter*, this book would not exist. I got back on Twitter in May of 2019 and proceeded to learn how to invite strangers into my life. One of those strangers was Jaime Dill. She has become my best friend, my other half. She doesn't just finish my sentences, she says the sentence aloud with me. Our lives overlap so much that sometimes I think meine geschitche is her history, that we are the same person, living with a touch of gentle madness in some sort of crack in the space time continuum. I could go on about all the ways she inspires me but that would be a long list. I'll just end this valentine by saying she gives me the strength to be the person I want to be and truly, my hero is my friend.

I believe that the universe (God, source, nature, whatever feels right for you) has a beautiful way of putting the pieces that you need in front of you. I know the idea for *Byline Legacies*—which came to Jaime and myself on the same exact day—was not a coincidence: it was big magic, as Elizabeth Gilbert would say. Writing is a strange alchemical process; the ideas come to you and it is your job to make them happen. That is the process as I know it.

I hope this book lets you experience the world beneath books. I hope each poet's truth has you falling in love with poets. I hope each super ars poetica moves you to compose elegies for the poems you almost wrote and odes on not writing. I hope the poetry lessons stimulate writing cats and dogs and the story shells you discover give you freedom in words. But most of all, I hope that when the day comes that you are writing your own author bio, receiving your first fan letter, and creating your own byline legacy, that you fondly remember the messages in this novel as the earthwork for your art. I promise you this: each and every person who reads this book will inscribe a significant line on my heart and I will not let you go.

—Lizzie Thornton, Editorial Co-Director

I'm trying to find the words to open up about what *Byline Legacies* means to me, why I wanted it to exist, and all I can do is cry. At first, I chided myself for this because my instinct is to always box my emotions in professional terms. But this book is my heart, it's all our hearts, ripped open and smeared on the pages. As much as we pride ourselves on being a community that supports one another (and we do it so beautifully!), we can't escape how lonely writer life can be. No matter how many times we see others expressing the same emotions, we still suffer insecurity, imposter syndrome, and irregular inspiration from the privacy of wherever we are. That is the moment *Byline Legacies* was created for, that hour when no one is commenting back to you, no one is checking in or by your side to push you along. In that quiet heartbeat of fear, you can pull out these stories and poems and see that you're surrounded by others just like you. We chose the pieces in this book because they are valid and honest. I have felt every one of these emotions myself at some point, so I can tell you with certainty that the whiplash you're feeling between loving words and hating their complications doesn't make you less of an author. It makes you more.

So, whether you're reading this in a high or a low, pleased with your work or completely vexed, it is my honor to speak on behalf of all the authors here and say—we've been there, and we're here for you.

— Jaime Dill, Editorial Co-Director

Jaime Dill

Byline Legacies

JESSICA SARLIN

Hey You

POETRY

JESSICA SARLIN is a freelance writer and artist from New Jersey. Heavily influenced by writers like Douglas Adams, John Irving, George Saunders and Kurt Vonnegut, she tends in her own writing to blend humor and pathos about the human condition.

After experiments with other vocations (land surveyor, pharmaceutical engineer, and martial arts instructor), she returned to her original Career Day choice from fifth grade: writer and cartoonist. Her writing style is still a childlike balance between dark and silly—a bit of humor in every tragedy, a bit of arsenic in every cartoon.

She is a member of SCBWI. In 2019, her picture book manuscript, *Sergio, The World's Greatest Dung Beetle Chef*, earned her a coveted spot in the PBChat mentorship program. Her poem, "Hey You," is a rallying cry to other writers who fall off the keyboard and continue to get back up again.

Jessica Sarlin

HEY YOU.
Have you ever worked long and hard
on a batshit crazy thing
to the point of bodily pain,
a new callous on a knuckle,
a piece of charcoal worn down to a nub,
half the clay in your hair and teeth
and you've forgotten to sleep,
screen-spent until your eyes are
drawn down to raw pinpoints
helplessly watching words shimmer,
go thin, and lose their meaning?

Then you stand back or rise from squatting
and regard what you've feverishly done,
only to realize in perplexity that you
have made a completely useless thing,
an object less important
than the crayon you started with,
a ridiculous piece not worth the breath of explaining,
that the divine mystery has bothered
to move you in a way that is not, it turns out,
the intricate, amazing work of a spider
but more like the mud left behind after a good wallow?

Yes?

Then scream in frustration and break all the pencils,
smash the teacup, pull the shades and surrender
to darkness or whiskey or doubt or all three.
We will wake up together in the same filthy clothes,

2

ready to try again,
to uncrumple the paper and re-view the face,
cry from laughter and say,
"Well, that's just perfect, isn't it?"

Because it is so LIFE-LIKE:
Messy and beautiful and useless and fleeting.

R. TIM MORRIS

How to Invite Strangers

FICTION

R. TIM MORRIS (b. 1975) was born and raised in Vancouver, Canada, where he works as a library technician at an independent school. His drive to tell original stories grew from his previous career of working in the film industry. He is married with two sons.

Morris has self-published four novels (*Molt*, *The Inevitable Fall of Tommy Mueller*, *This Never Happened*, and *To Be Honest*), as well as having edited and published a collection of short stories in 2020 (*More Time: A Brief Anthology of Indie Author Short Fiction*). All five books were published under his own imprint, Empire Stamp. Morris has had other works of short fiction published with Owl Canyon Press and the *Adelaide Literary Magazine*. His fifth completed novel, a dark fairy tale/fantasy entitled *The Lost Memories of Oceans*, was acquired by Fractured Mirror Publishing, release 2022.

In all of his works, Morris thrives on shaping his stories into intricate puzzles, begging the reader to question the parts they can't quite put a finger on (as well as the parts they *think* they can) and to take a second look at nearly everything.

You will roll your pant legs up, just below your knees, so you can feel the garden tickle your shins; the plants will quiver erratically from the summer gusts still blowing in and around towering buildings. Visions of your childhood will return: helping your mother pick the harvest from your modest backyard garden, softly squeezing tomatoes for ripeness, rubbing the foliage of aromatic herbs between your fingers, chewing on a mint leaf. Memories just like these will be returning more frequently. You won't be certain why. But you'll take another moment for the feelings to linger and to allow them to fade again.

The weight of the shears in your hand will remind you that you came up to the rooftop garden for parsley. Your tapenade recipe calls for three tablespoons of chopped parsley, and you almost began serving it to your guests downstairs before realizing you forgot the last ingredient for your canapé spread. It's an involved recipe, and certain steps of it are sometimes lost when left to memory. Snipping what you need, you will pause again for one last moment of quietude.

There's a fire escape which you use for rooftop access. The city's din always seems to reverberate through the suspended iron stairway. You will stop to hear it all—the good and the bad—with every footstep and with each grip of the railing. The day's heat still emanates from the metal too. You snake your way down three floors and back inside your apartment through the open kitchen window.

A couple of guests will be in the kitchen: she has mussed-up, jet-black hair and chapped lips, holding a drink unsteadily enough that anyone would know it wasn't her first of the night, and he is eating a plate of chicken wings like it's going out of style. Beads of buffalo sauce cling to his overgrown sideburns, glistening. They will be chatting in the way that strangers get to know one another, with small talk and unsure smiles.

You will eye them closely before realizing your bread is overcooking, smoke trickling out of the oven's slackened door. Without an oven mitt or even a potholder, you remove the tray and toss it onto the counter. The warped metal tray will spin around a couple of times in a lazy circle. Taking the parsley to the cutting board, you will chop it finely with a sharp knife, then mix the herbs into the tapenade, spread it on the bread, and top it off with some olive oil. The voices and shuffling of other people in your apartment echo off your bookshelves and hardwood floors. You will stop to breathe in deeply, then wonder why you continue to serve these people in your home. Something inside you will question your reasons for ever having invited them all in the first place.

A man you think you recognize will enter the kitchen confidently and lean over the counter across from you. You will offer him a canapé. He will refuse implicitly, but when you turn back to wash the knife in the sink, you're certain you see him taking one anyway. "I'll be right back," he'll say to you with food still crumbling from his mouth. The tiny head of a brown bird will be visible on his t-shirt, peeking out above the top button of the man's weathered coat. "Just got to wash my hands." You will direct him to where the bathroom is, but he'll inform you that he already knows.

Somehow, the couple who were previously in the kitchen will have disappeared. And though there is still a crowd in the next room, everything will suddenly seem empty. You will stop and think about past conversations, the things you wanted to say but got them all wrong, and how it might have been good to think them over first. Write them down, maybe. Things might have been different. Of course, they might have been exactly the same.

With the tray of canapés in your hands, you will stop at the door to consider those around you.

What brought them here?
Who brought who?
When will they leave?
Who will they be leaving with?

They will be an eclectic group. A woman chewing gum behind neon green lips. A guy in a wrinkled t-shirt that reads *Surf Tofino*, adjusting some of your coffee table knick-knacks. An older gentleman in a pin-striped suit and fedora, talking to a woman of mystifying beauty. She'll have eyes earth-brown in color and a shimmering crystal hanging from her exquisite neck. Both of them will be standing in front of your large oil painting whose only subject is a curious white tree. Two men, twins by all description, on the couch and looking like they'd rather be somewhere else. Another man on the opposing chair with a finger up his nose. And the canapé thief, who has still not washed his hands, will be surreptitiously discussing something with a young man in a faded red shirt and a leg in a cast, balancing awkwardly on crutches.

Who are they all, really?

How well do you truly know them?

The tray will suddenly feel heavy in your hands, and you'll place it on the floor. Right there, on the kitchen floor. It will try to shine beneath the light, though its sheen has been dullened by time's aching crawl. The fire escape will call to you, not for more herbs from the rooftop, but so you might take in the city once again. The city has never failed to inspire you. It never will.

There will be someone else outside already, a girl. She was not there before. She'll wave at you with one hand slowly, cautiously, opening her fingers in the same way as a flower might bloom. A train rumbles past in the distance. You will listen to it carefully: its heavy *clack-a-lack* clacking reminding you why you came to the city in the first place. Down on the street, late-night delivery trucks will be crisscrossing the intersection, a constant loop of the things people want, coming from here and going over there—a circle of unknown, perhaps empty, needs. Across the glass and concrete canyon, you will spy the dark silhouettes of people moving within dimly lit apartments. Some windows fuller than others, perhaps containing parties of their own.

Catching your thoughts drifting, the girl on the fire escape will point inside your own apartment and say, "A bit manic in there, isn't it?" Her sleeve will be covered in cat hair.

"I don't even remember inviting some of them," you will say.

"Sometimes we just show up. Is that what you mean?"

You'll pull your gaze from across the street and look at her—hair an unnatural white, the color of apple meat, if you had to describe it, and piercings lined up on one side of her face: eyebrow, nose, lip. "I guess some of you sometimes do," you will answer. Often it mystifies you, how quickly they seem to appear and depart. Their presence, whether there or not, leaves vivid impressions on your mind.

"We have the weirdest details, though, don't we? Me and all those people in there."

You won't be sure what she means, exactly, so you'll angle your head to question her further.

"Like, when I lie, I'll pull at my ear." She'll stop to tug one ear as an example. "And I lie about *everything*. Can't help it. It's a trait, I guess."

"Trait—?"

"A tic, maybe. We've *all* got them."

You will breathe in deeply, and there'll be something familiar in the air. A certain memory, maybe a reminder of how you felt in a different time. And by the time you turn back to the tiny bit of space the girl occupied, she will already be moving along, climbing back in through the window.

"You're leaving?"

"Only because I can't stay," she'll say with an ambiguous wink. "But I'll be around." She glides her hand through the air around her, as though simulating a leaf on a breeze. "Like those delivery trucks, I'll be here and I'll be there."

She's disappeared altogether when you finally go back inside. Someone will have placed the tray of canapés on the kitchen counter. Only a couple have been picked at, pushed around and poked into different spots on the tray. You frown at the remains, half-upset that they weren't all eaten. But you leave the tray where it is before walking into the next room. It will seem like a different crowd than before. Maybe it is. Maybe that's how it always goes. Now it looks more like a costume party, as if the intentions of the gathering itself have also changed.

There will be a boisterous, know-it-all guy in a bulky, foam Empire State Building costume. A disappointed woman in hospital scrubs. A sad man in a frog costume. Or is it a gecko? A dragon, maybe? Books will be scattered about indiscriminately. There's an ugly man hidden in the corner wearing a trench coat; dark feathery wings dangle ominously from underneath. An old woman with one eye of black and one of white.

A celestial sort of haze will overtake the room. A buzzing,

too, like a mosquito circling your head. You won't remember your walls being painted in Mediterranean blue, either. A song from long ago will be playing on the turntable, its melancholic opening notes returning long missed feelings to you.

Just as you are about to step out the window again for more air, a woman will catch your eye. At first, you find yourself thinking she's the same girl you just saw on the fire escape, but this woman is not really the same. Not really. Her head is shaved, a lip stud just enough off-center that you will question its placement. Electric blue cowboy boots. Her arms covered in tattoos, inked inscriptions, scribbled scripts.

You will ask her if she'd like to sit outside with you. You ask in a way that might sound as though you're simply continuing a previous conversation. She will click her tongue, disappointed in your proposal. "You can't keep going out there. Up and down that fire escape. You've got to mix things up."

Yes, you will think. *A change would be good.*

She will pull a cigarette out from somewhere, waving it winsomely, and then say, "How about you take me for a walk so I can smoke this stupid thing?"

As the two of you walk to the door, you will pass a seven-foot-tall spaceman of sorts. Incredibly, you had not noticed him before, towering above the crowd, in a golden, shining suit of armor beneath a dark hooded cloak and red-tinted goggles. He will be talking to a fairy, glowing amber-pink with butterfly wings. An actual fairy.

In the downstairs lobby will be a doorman in a colorful uniform; he will eye you indignantly as you and the girl in the blue boots exit the elevator, but you've seen him before and you know that's just his normal greeting. It's a tic, perhaps. Or a trait.

She will already have her cigarette lit as soon as you step out from under the awning and onto the sidewalk, leading you around the corner. Heat from the long day still lingers in everything, warming your skin as you pass. On apartment stoops and behind windows will be more and more people, as well as the ethereal glow of stories being told within. So many of them.

"They're no different from you, really," she will say bluntly, gesturing at the windows with her cigarette. "And they're all hosting the same parties as yours."

"All of them?"

"Most of them." She will take a long, long drag from her cigarette before sitting herself down on the curb. "Yours are better, though."

"My parties or my guests?"

She will simply smile a non-answer in the way that women in stories do, but real women always seem to do it better, you think. You will once again consider all of the characters you invited tonight, still taking up space in your apartment.

"Things we create will want to keep changing. They *have* to."

As you sit down beside her, it will feel you've already done so. Like you've played this sidewalk scene out in your mind over and over again. The gatherings behind windows continue, but outside it feels like a ghost town.

And she will place her free hand on your knee. Her head on your shoulder. And with a tear in her eye, she will say, "You still have something else worth saying."

"Not everyone will want to listen."

"You expect a lot from people, don't you?"

You almost say something else, but instead, you say, "They matter to me."

She will blow smoke from the corner of her mouth. You catch a wisp as it floats by, and the smell will remind you of something agreeable but from a more troubling time.

Then she will note your comment and say, "Only *parts* of them matter, though."

"Parts—?"

She will clear the lingering smoke away with a wave before turning to you, a stoic look on her face. "I only exist because of my name. That was all I was at first. Just a name. Then, all of a sudden, I picked up this guitar." She holds up a guitar case that you didn't notice. "And before I knew it, I had all this ink on me. This one"—with the wet end of her cigarette, she points to a tattoo on her arm that reads FALLING—"was one of the first ones."

You will run your hand along the tattoo, remembering each

letter.

Then she will say, "It's how *any* of us start out. *Her*, too."

A beautiful woman in brown yoga pants and a tight shirt will appear from nowhere, jogging along the sidewalk before stopping in front of you to stretch.

"Her? I don't recognize her."

"That's because I was only invited for my tits." Indeed, beads of sweat will glisten on her chest. She will shrug her shoulders nonchalantly, then add, "It happens," before running off again.

And then a man dressed in a white linen suit and a fake mustache will shout from across the street. "I only existed to quote Mark Twain," he will say. "And I didn't even get the quote right."

Next to you, the girl in the blue boots will nod in silent agreement. "It was all that any of us were at first."

Investigating your thoughts, you will say, "I was lonely." The street and sidewalk return to their ghost-like state.

"You're still lonely."

You will blow a rejected breath from your mouth, realizing that maybe now, the little details of everyone in your apartment don't matter as much as they used to.

She will flick the remains of her smoke across the street, all the way to the opposite sidewalk. And then, guitar case in one hand, she will stand up and point up to the rooftop with the other. "Don't keep tending to that garden you've got growing up there. Focus on the wildflowers instead. The ones that grow in all the places you haven't been. Or the places you've been too afraid to return to."

You will notice that your pant legs are still rolled up from when you'd allowed the garden to tickle your skin. But you will unroll the pants, already thinking about the next place you'll go.

Before walking away from you, she adds, "And this time, invite that one person you were always afraid to invite. Because you were embarrassed about your feelings for them. Because you didn't know how they might react. Or what they might say. Invite them in."

When you return home, the guests will all be gone. Your apartment will be cleaner than you'd left it, the books all back on the shelf.

In the kitchen, the canapés remain on the counter, still mostly untouched. You will eat one yourself—still enjoying it more than you should, maybe—before composting the rest. You will make yourself coffee. You will sit and you will wipe your eyes, and you will gather your thoughts.

And when there is a knock on your door, you will invite them in.

ELIZABETH BATES

[untitled]

PROSE POETRY

Wife and mother, ELIZABETH BATES, is a lifelong western Washingtonian where she now writes and teaches high school English. Bates' fondness of simple pleasures attracts her to meditations on distant eras and the natural beauty of her home as subjects for her writing. Irish poet, Robin McNamara, comments, " . . . the poetry of Bates ha[s] the ability to bring the reader to a place where nature gives hope and inspiration. Her poetry has an almost nostalgic look at Mother Nature and our relationship with her."

Bates is a novelist as well as a published short story writer and poetess. One poem earned her a 2020 Pushcart Prize nomination. Bates holds a MA in English from Southern New Hampshire University where she was honored with the university's 2020 Distinguished Scholar Award.

A self-proclaimed romantic-realist, Bates' writing often features a sentimentality conveyed through redolence of place, nostalgist ponderings of the past, and idealized renderings of reality. McNamara says, "Bates is an exceptional new talent in the poetry community and has proved herself to be a serious poetic voice with poems like "Capturing Nostalgia", with a nod to Hemingway and a bygone era of American life. Her poetry has the intellectual ability to make us think about what lies within ourselves and has the reader reaching out for more."

As I write a poem this wintry morning, I wonder which words I should pluck from the thesaurus to make it sound more beautiful—scratch that—eloquent—scratch that—hifalutin. I will mix this poem together like chili, adding ingredients as I go. A recipe, hopefully not for disaster—scratch that, calamity.

I toss in more than an em dash of dictionary—dollop of dialogue. A pinch of peppery pomposity and a smidgen of salty sophistication. No matter what I do, the flavor is wrong. No matter what I do, nobody will want to ~~eat this~~. Read this.

I step away, turn it down a notch.

Let the crockpot do its work, boiling things down to their essence.

The mixture is coming together fine, now that I've reached stanza five. The tomato paste splatters like marginalia on the counter, evidence of my haphazard process. I clean it up.

I think I'll leave my reader with this, as I close the final stanza and the chili simmers: a final stir of sobriquet, like "cool beans."

I don't know what I just made. But . . . it's *something*.

I think I'll toss it out now and start all over again.

EDEN CAMPBELL

The Process (As I Know It)

POETRY

As a child, EDEN CAMPBELL was continuously told that her father—a chronic runaway—was a writer before drugs took his life. Desperate for a shred of paternal identity, Eden picked up a pen and found that her imagination carried her far. In elementary school, her poetry won state-level competitions. In sixth grade, she wrote her first novel. In college, Eden wrote for, and edited, the school's annual poetry anthology. Over time, the magic of real life—of marriage and having babies—caught up to her and she set the craft aside.

In 2018, she took on a freelance position with a local nonprofit that assisted in the recovery of women rescued from sex-trafficking and domestic abuse, and in 2020, inspired by the discovery of a long-lost brother, she contributed her first editorial piece to *Severance Magazine*, exploring the aftermath of family separation. She has since contributed to *Thrive Global* and *Romper*, often discussing the trauma of abandonment, as well as grief.

Her writing has been described as, "Raw, yet endearing, with an emotional quality that is both touching and memorable. Eden addresses hard topics in a way that invites the reader to understand. She bypasses clinical jargon to speak the language of the heart." Her debut novel follows the story of a woman unable to cope with grief. Despite the hardship Eden has overcome, she hopes that whatever she writes inspires the reader to laugh and cry, as she has done for much of the journey.

I've been known to unwrap
a perfect square of rubbing alcohol and swipe
my computer's screen in an obsessive rhythm
until it shines
This is my process
    (Welcome to the madness)

I have an idea but ideas are like seeds—
picky little bastards—
who want sun and water
or coffee and candles
and a spiffy computer screen
They want peace
or possibly the soundtrack of melancholy
No, wait—
early 90s music
I'm painting the scene like an artist
    (only I can barely draw a stick figurine without
    it looking like a tree)
Story
on the other hand
is my specialty

"I'm sorry," I hear the usually subtle main character decree.
He drops to a knee,
and I gasp.

He has something to say immediately
    (though I'm still waiting on my coffee)

I am in love with him

with the integrity of the words he cries
No one cares for my story like he does

So I enter a strange dimension where
the words pour out
They are always impatient—the right words—
They slip in like a billboard along the interstate
commanding my focus as I scramble to articulate
Then, they're gone

And I'm managing these delicate pieces
as I dance between the kitchen
and my sanitized space
and back again

I'm often caught in this marvelous wrestling match—
lovesick for the story I long to tell—
where I'm changing music and
sipping coffee
inhaling the foreign scent of the candle I lit
    (which inexplicably makes me feel like I have it
    all together—I don't)

My character screams his apology
as my fingers meet the keyboard in a
clicking symphony
pounding out my truth
    (I mean his)
And suddenly nothing is sanitized

The candle's wick sinks beneath a pool of glassy wax

coffee chills like ice
computer screen smears
and I'm breathless because
I set the stage
I marched to the center like I wasn't afraid
I danced and sang, made a thousand mistakes
and brought a person to life
made you believe it was someone else
desperate for justice
and authenticity
and power
and love
I've come to realize
I don't need to sanitize
But I do it
knowing my insides will soon be
split
    (seems wise to prepare for such an onslaught)
I'm reckoning
with every question
I ever wanted to ask
and my characters
relentlessly pursue
the answers
All I do is listen
and write

The laptop claps as I close it
and it may be the only reaction
I ever receive
for what I've written

But I'll keep giving
myself to this craft
that inspires me
and rips me apart
Living art—
the characters in my mind—
I'll tell their stories
as long as I can tell mine.

GUITAR HANNA

The Cultivating Ideas Conundrum

NON-FICTION

GUITAR HANNA is an American Egyptian, raised in Southern California amid the Coptic Christian community. Her parents left Egypt in pursuit of the American Dream during the mid-1970s, thinking of a prosperous future for their children. However, this spirit of opportunity, prosperity, and success was challenging to achieve for a first-generation female immigrant who was late to understanding and reading the English language. With persistent determination and encouragement, Guitar vowed not to waste her education. She graduated from university with a bachelor's degree in Biological Sciences. Her love of science extended into a career in medicine and she currently practices pediatrics in Central Oregon.

Guitar shares her life with her Irish husband and together they are raising three multiracial daughters. They have become a world-traveling family, having visited fifteen countries in the past ten years. Guitar's journey of motherhood and her professional career have directly inspired her to write children's picture books that broaden young readers' understanding of our fascinating and diverse world. As an active member of SCBWI, attending writing conferences and participating in multiple critique groups, Guitar is dedicated to writing stories that foster growth and development, and perhaps shape the adults her young readers will become.

When it comes to writing, perhaps one of the most difficult aspects is coming up with an idea. *What's the topic? What's the story?* As a novice writer, the idea of "cultivating ideas" was daunting to me, perhaps because I simply did not know where to begin.

For the past twenty years of my adult life, I have devoted myself to a career in medicine. I have published scientific research. I have memorized medications, their adverse effects, and how they metabolize in the human body. I have studied the presentation of illnesses so that when faced with a sick patient, I can establish a quick differential diagnosis and the strategic steps to help heal their body. As an analytical thinker, the left side of my brain dominates.

When it comes to creativity, the right side of my brain is considerably weaker. I always knew I had the potential because prior to medicine, I loved the arts. I was quick to stand up and dance on any stage, sing in school musicals, enter art contests, and I loved reading novels from a young age. Unfortunately, I was told by my parents this creative side was rubbish. The threat of being disowned for following a path of creativity was real in my family, and too great of a threat. Thus, I shut down and ignored the right side of my brain.

As the years progressed, I established a successful pediatrics career, became a partner in a happy marriage, and began raising three delightful daughters. Despite having all these accolades, I felt incomplete as my basic creative instinct was hindered. The days dragged into weeks and the months crept into years, and it became evident to me that my discontent was secondary to my stifled imagination. I had enough of not following my dreams, and I decided to follow my heart's desire to write.

I spent six months writing my first picture book with a very particular vision in mind. I had no intention of writing anything else until I was signed by an agent for this specific book. In hindsight, I was foolish and arrogant. I dove into the querying trenches, and in the course of six months, I queried this manuscript to forty-three agents. Not one agent was interested. Rejections piled high, and I grew resentful toward writing. I had given a year of my life to this balancing act of juggling work, home, and writing . . . and I had nothing to show for it. I realized I needed help with my writing to become a good author.

As luck would have it, I soon found a freelance editor within the online writing community who challenged me and suggested I "cultivate ideas." When I hesitantly told her that I was unsure of how to pursue this challenge, she advised me to learn to appreciate what naturally inspires me, to identify conditions that innately foster my sense of curiosity, and to consider exploring my surroundings. I was encouraged and grew excited to develop new ideas.

I started by eavesdropping on my children since they were the same age as my target audience. A few of the silly things they said to one another sparked ideas, but nothing was really query-worthy. I read hundreds of picture books (literally) as "reading for research," better known as ReFoRe. This process was fruitful, and I learned which writing styles I enjoyed and those I did not. I discovered great mentor texts and authors whom I aspired to be like. However, I realized that my ideas were tragically lacking in comparison to those published stories.

I created a few ideas and tried to force them into a story, coercing them into foreseeable failed manuscripts. On the outside looking in, it appeared that nearly everyone in the writing community was either signing with an agent, contracting with a publishing press, or announcing their future publication dates. I was thrilled for my fellow writers but incredibly disappointed with myself for not succeeding as I had anticipated I would. I had never failed before, and I believed I was failing now. I felt an urgency to come up with something, anything. I came up with nothing.

My mind flooded with deprecating thoughts: *I'm not creative. I lack imagination. I will never succeed as a writer.* These negative thoughts impacted my mental and physical health.

Restless nights of tossing and turning interrupted my sleep. My left eyelid twitched all day, a clear warning sign from my body that I was familiar with as the twitch had first developed during my residency due to stress. My back ached and throbbed daily. It became clear to me that something had to give. I braced myself. I accepted the notion that I was not a writer, that I would never make it as a writer because I was missing that certain "je ne sais quoi" needed to become one. And so, I quit writing.

But who can blame me? I'm a full-time working mom! I was trying to balance my professional career, an ill family member, my marriage, my three young children, the pandemic, homeschooling said children due to the pandemic, and attempting to satisfy my dreams of becoming a published writer. Nothing in this tactic was balanced or headed in the right direction . . . and there certainly was no time and no place for me to cultivate ideas thoughtfully. I sacrificed my personal goals of becoming an author and, sadly, put away my writing notebook and pen into the dark crevasse of my little office.

Weeks passed. I was deflated. And my body continued to manifest externally what I was feeling internally.

Then, one gorgeous spring morning arrived. It was 10:00 a.m. and approximately 65 degrees. My three kids were begging to play outside and I needed fresh air, so outside we went. I laid out a picnic blanket for myself on the grass while the children rode their bikes up and down the sidewalk. I stretched and breathed and embraced the invigorating warmth of the spring morning sun while beaming with delight at the giggles of my kiddos. It was the first time in a long time that I subconsciously and spontaneously smiled. Seeing my daughters happy during the time of COVID put life into perspective for me, and I embraced my breath.

It was remarkable how a single, deeply inhaled breath rejuvenated me for a few moments. I wanted to keep that momentum, so I rolled over into my attempt at a downward-facing dog position to engage my breath and stretch my back a bit. I shut my eyes and inhaled slowly and deeply through my nose, expanding my lungs and filling my body with a sense of peace and calm.

I breathed in the crisp air of the earth, listened to the new life of baby birds chirping, and felt the sturdy ground beneath me. My mind was free, my back felt stronger, and my smile stretched freely from ear to ear. After five breath cycles, I opened my eyes and moved to lie flat on my stomach, resting my head on my hands and allowing my shoulders to sunbathe while I watched my kids climb the tree. The nagging sense of failure did not escape me, but as I watched my children summit the tree, I was impressed by their skill, determination, and technique with climbing. I was incredibly proud of them, and for a brief moment, I glanced to the grassy earth beneath me with contentment.

There, in front of me and my yellow house, on the tip of a grassy blade, sat a drop of water. The dewdrop glimmered in the morning sunlight, and I thought, *What is your story, little dewdrop?*

I laid close to Dewdrop, appreciating the slight reflection of myself in its mirrored surface. *Where had it come from? Where was it going? What was its journey like?* I ran inside, grabbed my notebook and pen, and dashed back out to my blanket. The first thing I created when my pen met the paper was the diagram for the life cycle of water: accumulate, evaporate, condensate, precipitate, and repeat. Then, I created columns with the three states of water: solid, liquid, and gas. I thought about the seasons and my children playing. The left side of my brain was finally merging with the right side. Later that day, I wrote a narrative before it evaporated into the clear blue sky. And when the day concluded, I had the first draft of a picture book.

From then on, I understood what cultivating ideas meant for me and my life.

I realized that inspiration will present itself to me when I'm most at peace, when my mind is not overwhelmed and racing with a thousand thoughts about work, marriage, children, school, home, pandemic, etc, etc, etc.

For some writers, the process of igniting inner peace may mean taking a long walk, a hot shower, or a therapeutic washing of the dishes. Regardless of the vehicle used, the end result is to achieve clarity in mind and peace within the soul in order to allow great ideas to take flight.

Saint Francis de Sales said it best: "Never be in a hurry; do everything quietly and in a calm spirit. Do not lose your inner peace for anything whatsoever, even if your whole world seems upset."

This difficult quest to cultivate ideas and ultimately write cannot be hurried or forced, nor pressured. To successfully develop and nurture great ideas, we must harness compassion and gratitude for ourselves and reclaim our breath.

ALLENE NICHOLS

After Writer's Block

POETRY

ALLENE NICHOLS was born to peripatetic parents in Paxton, IL, and raised in Illinois, Missouri, and Utah. By the age of ten, she was writing plays and performing them with the help of her two sisters. Her first poems were published locally ("My Country," by the *Peoria Wind Symphony*) and nationally ("The Children", by *Reach Magazine*) when she was fourteen. Her early work tended to be about nature carefully observed, social justice, and the personal cost of trauma. These themes have continued to be central to her work.

Allene had the good fortune to study creative writing under Gary Swaim, senior poet laureate of Texas, and Robert Nelsen. Her poetry and plays have been well-received. Her poem "Queer Salt" was a 2017 Outspoken Winner. Her sonnets have twice placed in the Poets Club of Chicago Helen Schiable Award, and her poem "Mushroom Dreams" was used to inspire a protest movement in Malaysia. Her poem "Chorus" was featured in the press kit for the anthology *Veils, Halos, and Shackles*. Her proudest accomplishment to date has been seeing her poem "Voice" in the anthology *Dance the Guns to Silence: 100 Poems for Ken Saro-Wiwa*, in which a poem by Amiri Baraka also appears. Her plays have taken Allene from Dallas, where Mark Lowry wrote in the Fort Worth Star-Telegram that "One Flew Over the Candy Cane" was "hilarious," to an off-off Broadway production of *Random Axe* by Looking Glass Theater.

From a young age, Allene has been an avid photographer, and her recent work has involved mixing image and text. In the forward to *Lifting the Sky: Southwestern Haiku and Haiga*, Penny Harter writes that Nichols's haiga, a photograph with a haiku embedded in it, "lift[s] us out of ourselves." Nichols's recent work has included longer poems and collections of multiple forms.

One day, the words won't wait.
They will tumble and roll,
kick and scream,
and birth themselves.

Hungry,
they demand paper and ink,
blood, the crow's call,
and the way sweat rolls
down my neck.

They wake me at night
to take me by the hand
and mash my fingers
on the keyboard,
brutal in their insistence,
tender in their release.

Then they caress me,
carry me back to bed,
whisper "we're pregnant"
and promise to bring forth
shrill-voiced infants
to wake me tomorrow night.

Only then do they let me sleep.

MARK TULIN

The Tea House Writers

FICTION

MARK TULIN (b. 1955) was raised in Northeast Philadelphia, and an only child. His father was a fruit man, and his mother was a housewife who suffered from mental illness. Tulin was not a good student in grade school, often getting into mischief and playing sports instead of taking home his textbooks. His English teacher in high school believed he had talent after turning in a short play based on *Hamlet*. Instead of pursing a creative writing curriculum in college, he studied psychology and became a psychotherapist. And for thirty years, he treated the most challenging families.

While living in Philadelphia, he published humor and poetry in several local papers and composed witty one-liners for disc jockeys. One of his humorous stories was read by a popular radio host in Philadelphia and received raved reviews. When Tulin moved to California in 2012, his writing took off and has since been published in over a hundred journals, magazines, and anthologies. Three of his short stories were read on podcasts, a Pushcart Prize nomination, Best of Drabble, and an honorable mention from Glimmer Train.

In 2017, Tulin began to write books. He wrote about his yoga experiences in a poetry chapbook called *Magical Yogis* (Prolific Press, 2017). He developed a connection to the Santa Barbara poor and penned *Awkward Grace* (Kelsay Books, 2019). He wrote a fiction/memoir book involving an asthmatic boy trying to survive his childhood, *The Asthmatic Kid and Other Stories* (Madville Publishing, 2020). His latest poetry books are *Junkyard Souls* (Alien Buddha Press, 2020) and *Rain on Cabrillo* (2021, Cyberwit).

I see Martin through the window at the Tea Leaf. He's a writer too: mostly non-fiction, memoir stuff. We worked on the high school newspaper together and still share many of the same literary ambitions. Both of us had a love for Hemingway's "A Moveable Feast," and fantasized about writing a book like that one day.

Martin is dressed in his usual woolen cap and overcoat, clothing that is generally too hot for Santa Barbara's warm weather. He doesn't see me right away and takes his place in line.

He is my only advocate in this lonely world of writing. We encourage each other and speak the truth, sometimes painful for us to hear, but we couch it in a way that has our best interests at heart. It helps to get feedback from another writer since we tend to be biased when it comes to our work, thinking that our stories are terrific once the letters hit the computer screen. Too often, we deceive ourselves into believing that our stories are perfect without any alterations, when in fact, we require many revisions.

Great, Martin sees me. I wave him to my table. We always sit at the same corner spot, under several colorful pictures for sale by local artists. There are patrons scattered around, working on their computers or sipping tea while staring out the window. The playlist generally changes each day, from contemporary to sixties rock, but today it's classical. The barista must have a new interest in music.

"Hi, friend," he says upon seeing me. "How are you feeling?"

I shrug my shoulders; no use talking about the pain in my side and the coughing spells that keep me awake at night. It would only bum us out, and we'd never talk about writing.

He puts down his tweed overcoat and herringbone Jeff cap on the seat and goes back to the counter for his tea. This time he chooses the Lemon Myrtle with a squeeze of lemon and honey. He says that Lemon Myrtle gives him energy without the jitters from caffeine.

"Sorry," the barista says, "we don't have any more croissants."

"No worries. I'll have a bagel with avocado, hon."

He always says "hon" to every woman, no matter how old. It's an endearing term that his mother often used. She called me hon when she was alive.

As Martin continues to have small talk with the barista, I work on my story. It's about a man who's about to jump off a ledge to his death when a crow speaks to him with a human voice. The crow's convincing plea results in the man changing his life. All I have to do is figure out what exactly the crow said to make the man want to live.

I take a sip of Chai Rooibos and watch the swirl of steam slowly evaporate in the air, wishing sometimes that I could be as light and free as the vapor. I hear the ping of my computer and reluctantly check my email, frightened of what I might find, assuming that it's another rejection. Some editors let you down too gently and others drop you like a sledgehammer. I know that it's part of the business, but I wish it were somehow different or that I wasn't so touchy about it.

It's an editor named Bentley Harris from a popular literary magazine. He says he enjoyed reading my quirky story, "Leaky Faucet," but it wasn't right for his publication—"although we can't accept this piece, I enjoyed your style very much and would like to see more." Every little bit of encouragement helps. That one goes into the victory column.

The ceiling fan creates a gentle hum as more people come into the Tea Leaf and take their place in line. I notice a woman in black yoga pants, the kind my wife used to wear. She loved her chai latte and also enjoyed putting me down. She was my harshest critic. "You can't write if your life depended on it," she'd say. "Your stories are too mundane, don't have good plots or interesting characters. You're wasting your time, Harry—you'll never get published. Why don't you do something more constructive like replacing our kitchen cabinets or fixing the broken fence in our yard?"

I shake my head, trying to get my ex-wife out of my thoughts, but it doesn't work. I still keep hearing her say what a boring loser I am.

Martin limps over to our table with his walking stick and pot of tea. He puts down the cane, which he claims was whittled from a branch of a hundred-year-old Moreton Bay fig tree, and places his Jeff cap on the back of the chair.

"Here's your bagel, sir," says the barista, walking toward us. "Do you need anything else?"

"No I think that will be it, hon. Thanks for asking."

Martin turns to me and gives me a wide-eyed grin.

"Did you hear about the workshop in San Francisco, Harry? There's this course on William Faulkner that I'm dying to attend. Do you want to ride up there with me? It's not until the end of January, so we have plenty of time to register."

"Sure," I say, despite not knowing how I'd feel by then.

Martin removes his cobalt-colored laptop from the light brown leather case that he recently bought and opens it up like a treasure chest.

He loves William Faulkner like I love Charles Bukowski. Martin writes everything in a stream-of-consciousness style that seems to spiral into a strange but exciting abyss. I often tell Martin that he's going to conduct his own William Faulkner workshops in San Francisco one day because he knows so much about him.

"What are you writing, Harry?"

"I'm developing a story that I wrote a few years ago into a novel."

"Yeah, what's it about?"

"A successful plumber leaves Pittsburgh and his wife and kids for Paris to be a famous artist and live in Montmartre. He learns to draw from YouTube and becomes extremely good at painting nudes."

"Where did you get that idea, Harry? That one's a real whopper."

"I read about a carpenter who abandoned his family to go to one of the Virgin Islands and became a novelist. Quite a successful one, at that. I just changed a few things around to make him a painter and his destination Paris."

Martin flattens the cap on his bald head, always complaining about a draft. You'd think he was more fragile than me.

"Nice idea, Harry. But, don't take this the wrong way: your plots are one-dimensional. When I read your stuff, sometimes it feels like a comic book—*bang, bang, bang.* A little more depth is needed to pull me in."

I pause a second to slow down my breath and not get defensive. I want to tell him to keep his opinions to himself, but I know he is giving me constructive advice, and that's what I want. Right?

"Plots are definitely my weakness. I get caught up with characters who seem to have comic book lives. I'm trying to slow down and make them living, breathing people, but it's hard. I get so excited that I speed through their stories."

Martin sees that I'm agitated, moves his seat closer to the table, and speaks in a soft voice. "Harry, I know you'll figure it out one day. I can feel it in my gut."

"I'm not looking for the book to be a runaway bestseller, Martin. My work might be too quirky for the general public. I just want to find an interested publisher who is willing to give an emerging writer a chance."

"Me, too, Harry. Did I tell you I started something new?"

"The story about the homeless couple you met at Oak Park?"

"No, I finished that one last week. I'm doing another piece about the years I spent in the Marine Corps. You know me. It's going to be in a stream-of-conscious style."

"A lot of psychological details, huh?"

"Exactly. You'll be the first to read it, Harry."

Martin is the only one I've told that I have prostate cancer and probably won't last a year. He never wants to talk about it and acts like I'm going to be around forever, always asking me to go places with him in the future, but I know he just tries to make me feel good. He can't accept that he'll be losing me, but that's not my concern right now. I have to complete as many works as possible so I leave a legacy. I want people to know who Harry Chambler was; he had an interesting perspective on life and wrote some memorable stories.

When I become too weak to write, I plan to give Martin all of my manuscripts to send out to book publishers. He promised to edit them for me if a publisher needs a few things done. I know in my heart that my work is good, no matter how many rejections I get. Like Martin says, "If you don't have faith in your work, nobody will."

When I'm gone, Martin will represent me. He will see my stories get published, my bylines and my acclaim. It will be as if he is the one getting published, and I know that will make him happy.

"Thanks, Martin," I say.

"For what?"

"Being a good friend and having faith in me."

"Anytime, pal. That's what we're here on earth for. To be good brothers."

I give Martin a hug. I don't want to cry, so I go to the counter and request more hot water to fill my teacup. The auburn-haired young woman at the register asks, "I couldn't help but overhear that you two are writers. What do you write, if I may ask?"

"I write literary fiction while my friend writes non-fiction, mainly memoirs," I say proudly.

"Wow, you two must be very clever. It takes a lot of skill to be a good writer. I'd really like to read your work sometime."

I wait for her to finish taking care of another patron.

"Thanks," I say. "The next thing I get published, I'll let you know."

It seems when one person encourages me, the universe is on my side. I don't care how long I have on this earth or how many years it will take for my work to get noticed; it will get done in the end. My cancer taught me that. Our bodies may go, but our spirits remain with other people, finishing our life's work.

Ping! Another email.

This one startles me, causing me to jerk the table, spilling my tea.

"Are you alright, Harry?" asks Martin.

"Oh, I'm fine," I say with a pained expression.

I read the email, then reread it. My hands are shaking and I feel a bit dizzy. Someone is interested in an old story I wrote about an elderly woman who was a kleptomaniac but only stole Kit Kat candy bars. I thought that piece of fiction was dead and buried, but now it has life again. The editor said that it was the funniest and saddest story that he's ever read and asked if I would be willing to make some small edits to fit the magazine's format. "Of course," I write back, "I'd be honored to be in your publication!"

I tell myself not to get so excited because it only makes me short of breath, and then I have to stick a pill under my tongue.

I put the warm teacup to my chattering teeth and hold it there in quiet excitement as I visualize my name on the front page of the journal with my story title. I'm going to buy at least a dozen and give them to my friends.

Martin is busy perusing the New York Times book section and circling the ones he wants to read with a red marker.

If I had enough strength, I'd stand up on the table and announce to all the tea-drinkers that I'm going to be published! Instead, I listen to my heart beating too fast and remember the doctor's orders not to get too excited. *Take a few deep breaths, Harry. Calm down, boy. You know your heart is compromised.*

I want to tell Martin about my story acceptance, but I figure it better to surprise him once the story makes it to print. If it doesn't get published, we'd both be upset. But I trust this magazine. They wouldn't be writing to me if they weren't sure it was worthy. It's one of those glossy journals with great art that is going to highlight my story perfectly.

It's funny how the world seems like a much better place when you get one step closer to your dream. Even death seems far away, not as scary as a few hours ago. Perhaps the feeling of hope alleviates some of this constant chaos in my body—the headaches, the fatigue, and the pain that goes from one organ to the next.

I feel my throat getting scratchy from all the medications and take a few sips of my Chai Rooibos, lean back in my chair, and gaze through the window at the tourists walking along State Street. My first thought is they will be living when I'm not, expanding their stories and relationships while mine have ended. I wonder how the world will change when I'm gone. Will this tea house still be here, and will Martin sit alone or find another friend to share his love of literature?

Many tourists come from different parts of the world, having unique stories waiting to be written: what he does, where she lives, what their relationships are like, and maybe the cancers they are fighting. It's all out there for me to embrace in these next few months, with however many breaths I have left.

Ping, Ping, Ping. A few more emails.
The sound of new messages no longer bothers me.

CARSON SANDELL

Crinkled Nights

POETRY

CARSON SANDELL (b. 2000) was raised in Santa Clara, California, once a home to fields of orchids, but now an overpriced, concrete wasteland. He said, "A path paved with addiction and isolation was laid out in front of me by my parents. If not for my brother, grandma, or my many mentors over the years, I would have gone down a road that's hard to come back from."

Carson's work has appeared in *Milkyway Magazine*, *Dissonance Magazine*, *Velvet Fields Magazine*, *Windows Facing Windows*, *Drunk Monkey Magazine*, and *Full House Magazine*.

His work can be described as emotionally evocative. Carson's work discusses childhood trauma with a rugged delicacy and manages to interweave small moments of happiness throughout his poetry. "And as emotionally challenging as my work can be, it is a journal. It's me making sense of my life, the pain, the sadness, and joy, through the medium of poetry."

[For Grandma]

your marbled miracles
marveled at my wilted lips
drooling mangled manuscripts
as if those undomesticated words
belonged in a mesmerizing menagerie
to awe people like Christmas light constellations

those lamplit nights
where blue carpet became
crumpled paper and my face
swallowed by my scraping palms
you'd enter and squeeze my shoulder
"You're one of the few people I believe in."

those crinkled nights
occur more often than not
but you taught me to unravel
palm-crushed pages like a noose's knot
so my face wouldn't be the poster child
for writers gone extinct without a single trace

MICHAEL PUDNEY

My Hero Is My Friend

NON-FICTION

Born in Leigh-on-Sea, an old fishing village in the southeast of England, MICHAEL PUDNEY has never caught a fish in his life. The eldest of four kids, Michael went through school with a holy trinity of aims consisting of not getting beaten up, avoiding detentions, and playing sports. Reading never played a role in his early life, passing him by like the fish he'd never catch at his local beach. The only reading Michael would bother with was on the back of cereal boxes to follow instructions to win a toy.

It wasn't until adulthood that stories took hold. Literary heroes such as R.L Stine, Roald Dahl, George Orwell, and literal heroes like Bernard Durrant, would set Michael on his path to turning his seed of interest into a blossoming love for words. His published works have included UK-based magazines and newspapers, a non-fiction piece in *Eastlife: An Anthology of Life Writing*, published by the University of East London, exploring extraordinary stories of East London locals. In fiction, Michael has won the People's Choice Award at the Williamstown Literary Festival in Australia and picked up best short horror story with Spinetinglers eZine. Michael does his best to keep his topics broad as he believes this keeps his knife sharp and stories limitless. He's had praise and criticism for his work, half probably accurate, the other half pretty accurate too. Here are some highlights: "Why don't you ever dedicate your stories to me?" —Jessica Pudney, Michael's sister, "I don't get it." —most readers, "You should do this as a job." —people who don't know how much writers get paid.

In Bernard's final hours, staring death in the face, he wrote a poem. The short piece contemplated what was to come and his lack of fear for it. He told us he was ready. He told us not to worry, that he wasn't in pain, and that he felt satisfied to have threaded his way into history through his published work.

It should not have come as a surprise that he had died. He was old. So, I should have been ready, but I wasn't. I still had so much unfinished business with the man who I knew had so much more knowledge than I could have ever consumed. Now, his novels and poetry would have to fill the void.

The guests were draped in black. They took up the first four rows in the church. I sat at the back—alone. I didn't want anyone to see me cry. What nineteen-year-old does? I hadn't cried at my grandma's funeral. I was sobbing at this one.

Sitting alone at his funeral was synonymous with the privacy and intimacy of our relationship.

Bernard Durrant was a writer, teacher, Second World War spy, and my mentor. And at ninety-two years old, he was dead. On this day, a piece of me would be buried with him, and it hurt like hell.

Years have passed, yet Bernard remains the single most influential person in my writing life. This is my homage to him and a nod in the direction of his extraordinary life. Bernard made me believe that writing was real, that writing was important, necessary, even. Somehow, he even made me believe I was good at it. Nobody had ever made me feel that way about the words I secretly wrote in bed late at night. He turned my embarrassment of writing among a social circle of literary-phobes into a passion for which to be proud. I fantasized that when I reached ninety-two, I'd be sitting at the window of my humble ninth-floor apartment, looking out at sea, surrounded by walls of books—some my own, reading and writing all day, every day. Utopia.

I believed that the validation I had slowly gained from him would sink away in the same soil that buried his body. I wondered if I'd ever find that elusive sweet spot again. When your biggest inspiration isn't there to inspire you anymore, is it possible to even *be* inspired? What does inspiration look like if not a wise old man?

His final request was for all funeral attendees to gather in the backroom and enjoy his work on display, like his own museum exhibit. This request was his final act, and probably his least humble. Humility was his strongest virtue—a tough one to find in people these days. Asking others to discuss his work without him there was uncharacteristic, but the circumstances were unusual, to say the least.

I couldn't do it. I left.

Not only could I not control my emotions, but my relationship with him felt so special, so personal, so unique, that I wanted to share it with no one. It was selfish of me, but I wanted to be at a spot I knew was special to him.

Bernard once told me he'd always felt a spiritual connection to trees, so I went to the local library gardens. I sat at a bench looking out at the mouth of the Thames through the arms and fingers of the trees. The view would not have been too dissimilar from his apartment window. I looked down at the order of service card, his face looking back at me from two different photos: an old black and white of a young Bernard I didn't know, and a colored photo of an old, fragile academic Bernard, the man I knew. I want to say I allowed myself to cry again, but in all honesty, I had no control over it. I tried to collect my memories—our memories, and thought back.

•

"You know the old man I clean for?" my mum said as she walked into the living room.

"You clean for lots of old men," I replied.

"Vincent."

"Oh, yeah. What about him?"

"He has this writer friend. I said you'd like to meet him." I winced. It was cliché. My feelings around writing had always been that it was a secret guilty pleasure, and meeting another writer wasn't going to change my opinion. And anyway, what were we going to say? What the hell do writers talk about exactly? The dictionary? I'd never "talked" about writing before. I just did it—alone. I put it off, but my mum managed to push me. And this push changed my life.

I knew the building. It was one of the tallest in our small town. Ten floors, maybe. The elevator was old, one of those where you had to pull across the heavy, metal grate. I got to level nine and Bernard was waiting outside his front door—a true gent. He was small, 5'9. Maybe he'd been a little taller before his spine had begun to take the shape of a question mark. He wore round glasses of simple design, and the white hair on his head was like beard stubble. His skin exposed his old age—a thin dot-to-dot of subtle blemishes and moles. He wore trousers, slippers, shirt, and a cardigan. He looked exactly like a grandad, though he had never started a family.

We shook hands, and I entered his small apartment. I noted his well-to-do accent—seldom found in this town. Just inside his hallway was a small metal man waving us through into his living space, which doubled as his bedroom. The books on the walls made the room the definition of cozy. He sat in his chair, perfectly positioned towards the window, and surrounded himself with everything he'd need to be an effective writer: books, paper, pen, tea, glasses. It was a writing station. He'd molded his surroundings optimally to suit his passion.

And then we talked. We talked about writing. We talked about our lives. It was natural, normal. It wasn't cliché at all. It was the kind of conversation I'd been looking to have for years. I'd been starved of a connection like this and I hadn't even known it.

I came out of that first meet up feeling like a writer for the first time in my life. I was invigorated, inspired to get down to it, to be as good a writer as I could because it was actually possible to be one. I had witnessed it first-hand from the work on his bookshelves and his work-in-progress that he'd shared with me. He was a writer in action, and I'd been behind the scenes!

•

Over the coming months, I would meet up with him around once every fortnight. Slowly, I'd draw life stories out of him, each richer than the last: that he was born with a hole in his heart and not expected to live past five years old—a story he was telling me in his ninety-first year. That he had lived in Japan for twenty-five years as one of the first westerners to teach English in the district of Sendai (the school where he worked had even named a dormitory after him). Or that he had worked for BBC Radio and written for the prestigious Woman's Hour. Or that he had interviewed The Quiet American author, Graham Greene. Or that he'd been a British spy during the Second World War who'd been caught by the Germans and subsequently became the longest serving British prisoner of war—the BBC even made a documentary on him. And this wasn't including his multiple publications of books and poetry. He oozed intrigue, and with intrigue came story.

I would write a piece and share it with him excitedly. He'd critique it and tell me what was wrong and what was right. I didn't have this at school. I'd never even felt like a writer at school. He was the teacher I had craved all this time.

He found me a short writing course to try, and by taking it on, I found myself putting pen to paper even more. This course turned out to be a gateway for studying creative writing as a real degree in a real university. My relationship with writing was quickly moving from a secret and sheepish hobby to a proud and public venture! Before meeting Bernard, I hadn't even known that writing stories could be studied. For a man who claimed to feel a special connection with trees, he'd certainly planted a seed with me.

But it wasn't just the writing element of our relationship that made me grow to love him. We would hang out as friends, regardless of our seventy-two year age gap. We'd play chess, or better put, he'd beat me at chess. We'd discuss worldly topics: politics, geography, sports, literature, and when he decided to turn his entire apartment into an electronic train town, I gave him a helping hand. I marveled at his ability to control tiny paint brushes for coloring tiny figurines with even tinier details without making one mistake. For a man without much time left, he seemed to make time stand still. He almost controlled it. Almost.

•

The biggest compliment he gave me was when he asked me to help extend one of his novels. I couldn't believe that he trusted little me with his published, acclaimed work. I felt validated. In a world once full of books too high to tip off the shelf, I was now taking my first step toward placing my novel next to the greats.

"My phone book has a small list of friends. I added your number. I hope that's all right. I do consider you a friend."

I blushed and pretended to play it down. But as I looked at my details in his phone book, wedged neatly between two other lucky contacts, my heart warmed. My hero considered me a friend. He closed the book then suggested chess. If I had known this would be the final time we'd pit our kings against one another, I would have tried to make the game last forever.

•

We never got around to finishing the extended version of Bernard's book because of his health. Time was, in fact, catching up with him. That hole in his heart began telling him the clock was ticking. I'd been visiting him for around two years, but the meet-ups were becoming less frequent. He wasn't fit for company and said he didn't want me over because he couldn't have me see him so weak and vulnerable. Maybe he sensed that I idolized him and thought that me seeing him in such a degenerative state would do something to damage that fragile pedestal I had placed him on. I'll never know.

I still have the working draft of our extended version of his book, unfinished, and unworked on since his death in 2011. I don't think it will ever be completed, and I'm not even sure I want it to be. I don't feel a desperate need to finish it. It was just a fun project we had together, and the key part of that is "together." Something not possible to achieve now, well, not in the physical sense. It's okay to let this one rest as it is.

Even at the funeral, I had learned things about him that we hadn't discussed in our meet-ups. He'd been married to a Japanese woman, for example. He'd also been in a major car accident in Japan. It struck me that the protagonist of the book we had been working on together also lived these experiences. The stories of his life were still being told, right under my nose. The mystery of the man remained even after his death, but it was clear there was still more digging that could be done. Even at his funeral, he had the power to fascinate.

We live in a world where everybody's life is so public, so well-documented and broadcasted that being enigmatic is seen as a red flag by others, something to be wary of. Bernard's generation was the last to embrace mystery, and he was a shining example of it. With his lifetime of tales, I learned from him the importance of story. Without stories, we are all just imprisoned experiences. On that bench, I made a vow between us that I would make storytelling my duty to the world.

I focused on my surroundings for that extra amount of time to wait for the natural world to come alive. After a few moments and a deep breath, everything transformed into its authentic self. A line of ants hauled their loads, birds spied their next meal, the sea bobbed in the distance—its crystal gloss bouncing off a boat's white hull. It was a warm day, warm like a hug. I recalled a line from his final poem, telling us not to be worried for him and that he was ready to go. Angels were standing over him and asking him to join the afterparty—he'd even grown wings. I had to trust him; he'd never let me down before.

But I missed him, and I still miss him now, a decade later.

He remains my core inspiration. I think about him when I need his help. What would he say about my progress as a writer? Would he think my work is worthy of publication? Would he read it and see improvement? Would I finally work out how to properly build a flow? I'll never know. What I do know is that Bernard made me believe in being a writer. He shifted my understanding of writing from being a childhood hobby—something to be shaken off like a bad case of fleas—to a way of life, a creative lens to see the world.

People often talk about how writing communities positively impact their craft, how they motivate, inspire, and give the opportunity for collective feedback. I agree these are important. For me, as a young novice with not an ounce of confidence nor insight into the writing world, all I needed was one person with the knowledge of a thousand people to guide me. He would give me that subtle nod of affirmation to convince me that I do belong in this elite club of writers.

And even today, when I have lost faith, lost my flow, lost my conviction, Bernard is there, and he nods. And I write.

MARCO SANTOMENNA

Freedom in Words

POETRY

MARCO SANTOMENNA (b. 1987), grew up in New Jersey. As a preteen, he was introduced to writing through his grandmother, Joan Santomenna, who was a published author. Together the two developed a middle grade novel which Joan self-published. Over the years, Marco grew more and more interested in writing his own stories, starting with flash fiction and poetry before finally developing his first novel in 2018, *The Arch*.

As the years progressed, Marco developed *I Am Nobody*, a middle grade story about an anxious superhero, and *The Spark that Burns*, a young adult story about an immortal teen forced to choose between embracing violence and saving the world. His flash fiction story "Under Pressure" was published by Gestalt Media in 2020, followed shortly after by the publication of his poem "Freedom in Words" by Cardigan Press.

—A crinkled sheet of lined paper and a weary pencil—

Alone again, punished for being myself,
ignored on the school ground, everyone else having fun.
The bully's fist reminds me of my place.

> Dented armor clanking against the shield,
> I am alone, hope abandoned.
> Nothing left on the field but broken
> weaponry.

Blood dripping on the page,
smudging as I wipe it away.
The pain dulls from experience.

> My enemy sneers in victory,
> surrounded by the cheers of their
> followers.
> Confidence built with power from fear.

The tears threaten to flow,
I grind my teeth in resistance.
It has to end.

> A dark cloud brews in the sky,
> red wings of fiery doom
> appear.
> Flames lick the sky in search of
> prey.

They're coming for me again,
they'll never leave me alone.
It's time to stand.

> I raise my sword in defiance,
> a hero keeping the dragon at bay.
> The great beast hesitates at the renewed opposition.

A hand comes into view,
offering to pick me up, with goodwill and a smile.
A new friend, a stoic ally.

        The sun rises in the east bringing hope,
          shining on the armor of comrades.
      Colorful banners wave as I charge to victory.

—Pencil poised on the page, hopeful and defiant—

CAROL BETH ANDERSON

Coffee-Shop Writer

FICTION

CAROL BETH ANDERSON (b. 1977) was born and raised in the Arizona desert, where she played make-believe games with her twin sister and older brother, transforming blankets into princess capes and her mother's dresses into fine gowns. Almost as soon as she learned to write words, she began turning them into stories.

Beth graduated from college with a degree in Theatre/Drama. As an adult, she moved to the Austin, Texas area where she periodically returned to creative writing via blogging. For decades, she said she wanted to write a book "someday." In 2017, *someday* turned into *now*. Beth met a local author, read her book, and thought, "I could do that." Hours later, she started brainstorming a YA fantasy series, the Sun-Blessed Trilogy. She published it in late 2018. Beth published The Magic Eaters Trilogy, an upper-YA fantasy series, in 2020 - 2021. Blogger Sara Cleveland reviewed the first book, saying, "Anderson's characters are wonderfully imperfect creations . . . *The Frost Eater* is hands down the best YA book I have read in a long time. Maybe ever. Someone give this woman a movie deal and then don't botch the adaptation, please."

Beth has also published a book of fifty-word stories titled *The Curio Cabinet* and a guide for fellow independent authors called *Early Readers Catch the Worms: How Alpha, Beta, and ARC Readers Can Help You Publish a Better Novel.*

In addition to writing, Beth enjoys baking sourdough bread, hanging out with her teenage kids, husband, and miniature schnauzer, and hosting high-school exchange students.

"Are you L.E. Higgins?"

My hand freezes halfway to my purse. It's the first time a stranger has ever recognized me. I'm oddly terrified.

"The author of *Small Town, Big Shoes*?" the barista prompts.

Her enthusiastic voice drowns out the soft jazz playing in the background. I could swear every one of the store's recessed lights is pointed at me. I remind myself to smile, and my lips spread way too wide, like a second-grader who was told to "say cheese."

"That's me!"

"I'm a big fan." She grins. It's a great smile with a little gap in the middle, the kind of detail I always find myself noticing. "It'll be four eighty," she says.

"Oh!" This is the second time she's told me the price. I instruct my hand to continue its journey into my purse. As she swipes my credit card, I give the people in line behind me an apologetic smile.

"I'm looking forward to your next book!" the barista says. She must be about twenty-five, decades younger than me and most of my readers. I imagine her holding an e-reader and downing Red Bull as my other fans read paperbacks and sip Ensure. I can't help but adore her.

"If you want something to read in the meantime," I say, "I'm publishing a serial story on my blog."

"Like, breakfast cereal?"

I chuckle. "No, a long story told in small bits. I usually post a couple episodes a week."

Her brows—shaped into Instagram-worthy arches—leap up, and I'm pretty sure I made her day. She nods, the messy bun atop her head bouncing. "I'll check it out!"

She hands me my receipt. I scrawl in a tip and sign it, then scuttle out of the way of the next customer.

"See you later!" she calls.

I can't tell if this is her customary goodbye or a hopeful request, so I just wave with a little laugh that comes out way too shrill. I fiddle with the clasp on my purse, afraid if I look up, I'll discover that every eye in the place is fixed on the cackling author who held up the line.

I'm back a few days later, and the same barista welcomes me

with the same sunny smile. "Ms. Higgins, hi!"

This time, there's no line behind me, and my smile feels more natural. I shove an errant dark-blonde curl behind my ear. "You can call me Lydia."

She draws in a delighted gasp.

I barely hold back a chuckle. "What's your name?"

She gestures at the blank name tag pinned to her red apron. "They said I'll have a name next week." This time, I do laugh, and she joins me. "I'm Jemma," she says.

"Well then, Jemma, I'll have a small mocha." She can't seem to find it on her register screen, so I point. "Top right." A couple years of ordering the same three drinks over and over and I know the register a little too well.

"Oh, there it is!" She enters the order and looks up. "Four twenty-seven." As she runs my card, she says, "I love the story on your blog."

"I'm glad you're reading it!"

"Something's gotta hold me over until your next book comes out." She looks down to tear off my receipt, and the light catches her earrings. Heart-shaped rhinestone studs, exactly like the ones the barista in my serial story wore in my most recent episode.

I mull that over as I wait for my drink. Today, instrumental versions of pop hits are playing from the shop's speakers. When I take a deep breath, I note a hint of cinnamon in the cool air, tempting customers to try the fresh scones in the glass display case. I scan the room to choose a table. Only one is occupied, taken by a young mother with a sleeping baby strapped to her chest.

Once I've got my mocha in hand, I sit next to a window and open my laptop. My novel manuscript is right in front of me, but those earrings are all I can think about. Did she buy them to match my character? Did my subconscious notice them last week and write them into my story? Or is it just a coincidence?

If I wrote thrillers, I'd probably be creating a whole story in my mind about how the barista is a seemingly cheerful stalker with a dark streak. But I write heartfelt, small-town tales. Like *The Waltons*, but with less calico and more kisses. To me, those shiny earrings are simply an intriguing connection between my reader and my story, Jemma and me.

And all at once, I have an idea, something that makes me cover a silly grin with my coffee cup. I leave my novel untouched and open a browser tab to write another installment of my serial.

As I write, I keep stealing glances at Jemma, who's busy making drinks, though no one else has entered. Someone must've put in a mobile order. When she finishes, she comes out to wipe down some tables, and I get a good look at her. Beneath her blue apron, she's wearing high-waisted jeans and a wide-necked yellow crop top over a white tank. On her feet are well-loved Mary Janes with roomy toes, perfect shoes for someone who stands during their whole shift.

I'd never write a real person into a story, but there's nothing wrong with stealing little details, right? So in this episode, I describe my barista's brown, buckled shoes with scuffs on the toes, just like Jemma's.

Four days later, I wait in line, then stroll up to the counter, where Jemma's forehead is glistening with sweat like she just finished a workout. It's the tail end of the morning rush.

Her face brightens when she sees me. "Lydia! Hi!"

"Good morning! I'll have a medium latte." She goes still, gaze fixed on the register. "Middle of the screen," I say. She swipes my card, and as I wait, I notice her nails. They're so short that I'd bet she bites them, but today, they're painted a lovely salmon color. Just like the barista in my story.

I catch her eye and realize she saw me looking at her hands. A fun-loving grin takes over her face, and she looks even younger than usual.

"I like your nail polish," I say.

"Why, thank you," she says with a giggle, glancing down at her shoes.

I find myself giggling too because *she knows I know she knows.* I almost expect her to say something about it, but instead, she asks, "When did you decide to become an author?"

I glance behind me to make sure no one is waiting, then launch into the same origin story I've told a dozen interviewers, about the annual physical I had shortly after my fortieth birthday.

I'd filled out a health history form, and as the doctor read my essay-length answer to a question about my exercise routine, he insisted I should write a book. I then ask her about her hobbies, and we continue chatting about everything except nail polish and Mary Janes until someone else walks up to the register.

Over the next few months, both baristas continue imitating each other. Thankfully, Jemma never does anything drastic to look like my fictional character—she doesn't go under the knife or get green contact lenses. And I don't change my original description of my character's body, face, or hair.

No, this exercise is all about the little details. My barista wears a silver ring like the one on Jemma's pinky; Jemma wears acid-washed overalls identical to the ones I gave my character. The two women share hair barrettes, capri pants, and a particular pair of unmatched socks that I couldn't stop laughing about one morning. Neither Jemma, nor I, ever mention our game of mutual imitation.

On a Tuesday in mid-March, I arrive at the coffee shop, sleepy from a night full of plot points bounding through my brain, vying for attention. I order black coffee with three shots of espresso.

"Wow, Lydia," Jemma says. "You're hardcore today."

I can't help her find it on the register screen because goodness knows, I've never ordered it before. Her search for the drink on the screen takes at least a full minute, giving me plenty of time to take in all the details of what she looks like today. Her name tag (imprinted with her name now) has a hand-drawn shamrock on it. She has a new, rose-gold metal band on her smartwatch. And instead of wearing her brown hair in a messy bun, she's put it back in two braids. Braids would be fun, I think.

"Found it!" She looks up with that cheerful smile.

Maybe it's my sleepiness tearing down my inhibitions, but I hear myself saying, "You know, Jemma, you inspire me."

Her smile fades, and for a minute, I think I've upset her. Then I realize she's blinking hard, eyes shining. "No," she says, "it's the other way around."

The interaction sticks with me all day. That night, I'm scrolling through my tablet looking for a show to stream. The action reminds me of Jemma searching for drinks on the register screen. I stop what I'm doing, my brows drawing together.

I've spent so much time focusing on Jemma's appearance. Our game requires attention to detail, after all. But over the course of four months, we've had countless little chats across the coffee-shop countertop, and I've gained deeper insights into her too.

I've learned that Jemma lives and breathes stories, not just mine. She's a passionate fan of more books than most people could name, from space westerns to the types of romances that make me blush.

I've learned that she's creative. She's told me she makes many of her accessories.

I've learned that, as great as she is with people, Jemma struggles with the basics of being a barista: the register screen confuses her, she forgets the difference between a latte and a cappuccino, and the morning customer rush has never stopped overwhelming her. Somehow, I know it's not that her brain can't handle details. She's simply too focused on the journeys her imagination and creativity take her on.

I'm exhausted from my night of little sleep, but I'm too keyed up to go to bed. I sit at my laptop and pull up my blog. The serial will come to an end soon. I've had the last details of the story planned out for months.

"Can I change it now?" I ask aloud.

My cat meows as if to say "yes." I'm glad to know my room-mate believes in me.

I type, letting the story meander in a new direction. My fingers fly faster than ever when the barista enters the scene. I write about her anxiety as she approaches her boss at the end of a shift. The deep breaths she takes. The blush that warms her neck and cheeks, the moment she almost chickens out, and finally, her decision to speak, despite her fear.

"I'm giving my notice," she said, her voice wavering.

Jamal's brows drew together. "Why? Is there anything I can do to—"

"No." She hadn't meant to interrupt him, but now that it was done, she plowed forward. "I've got dreams, Jamal. It's time for me to follow them."

I finish the episode in record time. The next morning, I edit it and hit publish. A day later, I'm back at the coffee shop.

"I liked your most recent episode," Jemma says.

"I'm glad!"

"It feels like the story is gonna be over soon."

"You're right."

"Bummer."

I shrug and smile. "*All good things* and all that, right?"

"Do you think you'll do another serial?"

"I'm considering it. I might even do a spinoff with one of my favorite characters. I don't think her story is over yet."

Jemma's lips part in a wide grin.

Our game continues until a couple of weeks later when I walk into the coffee shop and find the manager at the register.

"Lee!" I say. "I haven't ordered from you in ages."

She gives me her friendly, professional smile. "I'm filling in until we find someone else for the register."

"What about Jemma?"

"She quit. But at least she gave notice. Most people don't these days."

I hate the word *bittersweet*; in stories like mine, it's terribly overused. But it's the only good description for what I feel right now. I hope Jemma is following a dream. I hope she never has to search for items on a register screen again. And yet . . . "I'll miss her," I say.

Lee chuckles, something she doesn't often do. "Oh, she's still here." She points to the tiny table in the corner, near the bathrooms.

There's Jemma, hair loose around her shoulders.

I order, and while I'm waiting for my drink, I saunter to Jemma's table. She's typing furiously on a laptop, and I know I shouldn't look, I really shouldn't, but—

Chapter Two, it says at the top of the page. A rapidly growing paragraph of text follows the heading.

I lay a hand on Jemma's shoulder and squeeze.

She looks up. Her perfectly shaped eyebrows rise, and she gives me her white-toothed smile. There's something different in it today, something both serene and excited. "Hi, Lydia." Her smile widens, something I wouldn't have thought possible. "You inspire me."

"No." I have to swallow before I can continue. "It's the other way around."

LYNN KATZ

A Writer Reading Charlotte's Web

POETRY

LYNN KATZ was born in upstate New York. Eager to explore the world, she earned degrees in Washington, D.C., Grenoble, France, and Syracuse, NY. She taught school in Massachusetts and the USVI, and eventually settled in Connecticut to raise a family. Her debut novel, *The Surrogate*, began to germinate in the aftermath of the Newtown, CT mass shooting, a national tragedy that took the lives of twenty first-graders and six educators. *The Surrogate* explores the psychological profiles of a would-be mass shooter and the high school English teacher who tries to help him. "Lynn Katz weaves together a compelling story that manages to raise all the key questions. What is the role of parenting and gun culture in producing the (mass)shooter? [. . .] With a series of surprise twists that will leave you on edge, Katz thoughtfully illustrates the issues while establishing herself as a first-rate storyteller."—Harold I. Schwartz, M.D. Psychiatrist in Chief Emeritus, the Institute of Living/Hartford Hospital; Professor of Psychiatry, University of Connecticut School of Medicine

Katz has written three contemporary middle-grade novels that also grapple with serious issues impacting children, from divorce, to hoarding, to childhood cancer, to domestic abuse. Despite these serious topics, Katz weaves humor and hope into every story. She also finds authentic ways to include references to her favorite book in her writing: "Everything I need to know I learned from reading *Charlotte's Web*."

"Where's Papa going with that ax?"
grabs hold like a tick on a dog's back.
The smell of bacon drifting through the farmhouse
means more than a hearty breakfast.

Fern Arable,
a name chosen randomly
from a Maine telephone book?
Not likely.

What a rat says—
not the best predictor of what a rat does.
Buttermilk baths,
kind salutations,
plucked from the vine
like ripe strawberries in June.

A simple message glistening in a spider's web or
hovering above highways on billboards,
changing the world.

One word at a time.

JANE SCHAPIRO

My First Fan Letter

NON-FICTION

JANE SCHAPIRO (b. 1956) grew up in St. Louis, Missouri. Schapiro didn't discover writing until after college, but she credits her mother, a book reviewer and editor of a small literary magazine, for instilling a respect and appreciation for words.

Schapiro is the author of three volumes of poetry. Her first book, *Tapping This Stone* won the Washington Writers' Publishing House Award, (1995). Poet C.K. Williams wrote, Schapiro "can find the poetry in pain, the sympathy in the imaginary." *Let The Wind Push Us Across* (Antrim House 2017) is Schapiro's account, told through poems and photographs, of her and her sister's 3,500 mile cross-country bicycle trip. *Warbler* (Kelsay Books, 2020), her most recent book of poems, won a 2020 Nautilus Book Award. Poet Rennie McQuilkin wrote "There is much melancholic beauty in the book's dirges and toward the end, splendor has the last word."

Schapiro is the author of the nonfiction book *Inside a Class Action: The Holocaust and the Swiss Banks* (University of Wisconsin, 2003) and a chapbook *Mrs. Cave's House* (2012 winner of the Sow's Ear Poetry Chapbook competition).

"Often, people, when learning that I write poetry, ask me what my poems are about. I used to struggle with the answer. But then I came upon a quote from poet David Ignatow that answers the question perfectly: 'My avocation is to stay alive, my vocation is to write about it.'"

Schapiro lives with her family in Northern VA.

I have a fan. His name is Ron. He lives in Kansas.

His letter arrived on a Friday; I remember because all three children were out of the house and I actually had the chance to write. But I wasn't writing; I was stewing. I was sitting in my chair fretting over my latest rejection. An agent who was all set to represent my true-account story of four 1994 Bosnian Olympians changed her mind. A little misunderstanding. She thought they would be in the 1998 Olympics. Without that assurance, what's the point? It's just an exciting story. Who can pitch that?

I was sulking in my chair. Goodbye, Terry Gross. Goodbye, book tour. Goodbye, bestseller's list. Goodbye, potential readers. With one phone call, my fantasies were erased, my career once again a blank sheet. That afternoon, I waited a little longer to make my daily sojourn to the mailbox. Normally, while walking to the mailbox, I prepare for rejection. I do deep breathing and visualize the self-addressed stamped envelope, how it looks, how it feels. I enact the moment of confrontation between my name and myself. On that Friday, I did none of those. I blankly stared ahead, too depressed to care. There, in the mailbox, on top of the Victoria's Secret catalog, was an envelope addressed to Jane Schapiro. Schapiro—that's my writing name. The envelope was not my envelope. And it was thin. Could it be? I looked at the return address—Ron from Topeka, Kansas. Think, think, *what editor do I know named Ron in Kansas?* My heart raced. I ripped it open.

> *Dear Jane,*
> *Well, I suppose this is a fan letter. Never written one*
> *before, so I'm not quite sure how to proceed.*

This must be a joke. A chain letter.

> *I came across your work . . . I loved your poems . . .*
> *Is there—or will there soon be—a collection of your*
> *work? I'm hoping that one exists or is in the works*
> *because I'd love to read more.*

I looked around the corner. Where was the mailman? I looked at the envelope. It was postmarked and stamped. This had to be real! This was an honest to goodness fan letter. *Who needs a Muse? I have an angel. His name is Ron. He lives in Kansas.* I rushed into my car and raced to my husband's office. He was on the phone. I shoved the letter in front of him. He hung up. I waited for a smile, a hearty congratulations. "Where did he get your address?" he bellowed. "He never should have been given your address. Remember what happened to your sister? Followed by some academic nerd who heard her deliver a paper at a conference. We need to call the magazine—" I was out the door. I'll take my chances. So what if Ron is a stalker? He likes my poems.

Immediately, I began composing a response in my head.

My dear dear Ron,
You'll never know what your letter meant to me.

Overdramatic. Sentimental.

Dear Ron,
Sorry for the delay, I'm in the middle of writing a novel.

Arrogant. Elite.

Dear Ron,
I am sending you a signed, complimentary copy of my book.

Desperate. Needy.

I decided to wait a few days. Get used to the idea. Chill out. If I wrote back too quickly, he'd think he was my only fan, that I had nothing else to do. But I couldn't get him out of my mind. Every morning I'd wake up and repeat to myself, *I have a fan.* Every night before drifting off, the same mantra replayed. I found myself daydreaming. What does he look like? Where does he work? Is he married? An intellectual? A family man? Before I knew it, I had become a fan of my fan. I dreamed of meeting up with him one day. We'd be seated next to one another on an airplane or at a lecture. . .

For weeks the thought of him kept me going. I no longer felt invisible. I'd walk into a bookstore, see all the exciting stories that were being told, read the blurbs on the back and say to myself, *it's okay, remember? I have a fan. His name is Ron. He lives in Kansas.* This refrain saw me through all my chores, all those daily obligations which in the past only added to my feeling of invisibility. Waiting in carpool lines, making dinner, washing dishes—*I have a fan. His name is Ron. He lives in Kansas.*

Finally, I decided it was time to move on. I was becoming too obsessed. So, I wrote my letter back. It was cordial, gracious, and professional. Included was a brochure so he could order my book directly through the publisher. So what if I have two hundred copies sitting in cartons in my basement. I decided it would be better if we kept our distance from one another. When push came to shove, I realized that I didn't want to strike up a correspondence with him. He could only be an authentic fan if he remained anonymous. Otherwise, he'd be a friend, an acquaintance, a pen pal, a colleague. I had enough fans who were people I knew. My mother made sure of that. I wanted to keep my one bona fide admirer.

I never heard back from him. I stopped expecting to find a letter postmarked from Kansas when I reached into the mailbox. I stopped wondering where he was or what he was doing. I no longer repeated to myself *I have a fan* in the middle of the grocery store or while doing laundry. In fact, he is largely forgotten—his letter stashed away with other acceptance and rejection letters. Except, sometimes, when I write. During excruciating moments when I am staring at a blank page, when no word or rhyme seems strong enough and futility reigns, when I am alone and struggling with my aloneness, I remember him and repeat:

I have a reader. His name is Ron. He lives in Kansas.

JONATHAN PETLEY

Sonnet Twenty Twenty

POETRY

JONATHAN PETLEY (b. 1977) was raised in Eastern Virginia and shares his creativity with his twin brother; at a young age they discovered the fun of using their imaginations to create and problem-solve together. Jonathan experimented with artistic expression as early as three or four years old, when he drew his first train on the hardwood floor of his parents' living room. Jonathan wrote a lot of poetry throughout his childhood and adolescence before his artistic endeavors shifted mainly toward the visual arts. In the past several years, however, he has returned to writing with an interest in poetry and children's fiction. He enjoys poetry because it engages his creative mind without being subject to some of the rules of traditional story-writing, and results in short bursts of personal expression.

Jonathan has self-published two picture books: *Big Juice* and *The Big Surprise*. He is proud of *Space Doxie*, a collection of comic strips based on the personality and antics of his real-life dachshund and his love for space and science-fiction themes. Jonathan was named a finalist in the 2021 "Fifty Precious Words" writing challenge, and currently illustrates for Sage's Tower Publishing. Additionally, he is honored to be included in this anthology, among so many great writers—"I love the idea of sharing something completely new with the world."

Jonathan enjoys creating work that anyone of any age or background can appreciate. His most significant influences include Shel Silverstein, Robert Frost, Maurice Sendak, and Dr. Seuss. He is a fan of structure, meter, and rhyme, but only when it works; sometimes the words make their own rules, and that's okay too.

While winter chills await the April parch,
The world is set to change in many ways.
Were Shakespeare's words *Beware the Ides of March*
Much more than just a clever turn of phrase?
As screens light up and billions sit and sulk,
Cooped up within a cut without a scene,
I pride myself with props procured in bulk
And wonder what it means to quarantine.
Yet still exists my latent sense of hope
As summer sleeps behind the heather sky.
These times have taught me many ways to cope:
I live, I laugh, I love, I muse, I cry.

My quill is dipped in months of death and doubt,
To redefine what life is all about.

KATE KENZIE

The Ghost Writer

FICTION

KATE KENZIE is an avid reader who book blogs on From Under the Duvet and Kate Kenzie Writes, and always wanted to write a novel but pushed the dream aside until ill health meant she spent too much time at home and under the duvet. Like reading, she discovered writing is the perfect form of escapism and legitimizes her daydreaming nature.

The blogging community encouraged her to join the Romantic Novelist Association's New Writers Scheme. Being part of the scheme has opened up her world and has given her the support she needed to finish the novel and other work. She is drawn to books about relationships and the supernatural, so her work often reflects that.

Kate lives in East Yorkshire, UK, surrounded by books, her dogs, and her family. Her aim is to bring a little piece of Yorkshire to everyone, with a sprinkle of magic.

Paradise was starting to feel like a mistake. The stack of well-thumbed creative writing books taunted Emma, while the blinking cursor on the blank document criticized her procrastination. The notebook she'd bought weeks before remained closed, despite the anticipation that first inspired her.

There were no words.

No ideas.

Nothing.

All the tricks she'd collected from hours of reading and browsing social media for tips on tackling writer's block had failed. She'd strolled in the countryside for fresh air, tried rewarding any words with a sticker, and taken her notebook to the local coffee shop for a change of scenery. Instead of an in-depth exploration of character, her free-writing exercise led to a five-page tirade on how novel writing was too difficult. There were no flashes of inspiration, not even a spark.

She slumped in her chair and pushed it away from the antique walnut desk. There was no excuse. She was not forced to balance her laptop on her knee while sitting on the sofa here, nor did she have to huddle over the tiny kitchen table surrounded by the bustle of the household. This room was silent. She had space to spread out and work. The study, lined with bookshelves brimming with leather-bound tomes, was a writer's paradise. The earthy aroma of the leather mingled with the comforting smoky embers in the hearth. If she could not write here, maybe she was the fool her family thought she was and deserved to fail.

Their faces loomed in front of her as she recalled their shock when she blurted out her intention to take a writing sabbatical once her redundancy money came through.

No, she was not going to jump straight into the search for a proper job as her father requested, nor return to education to further her prospects as suggested by her older sister. The idea of finding a husband and starting a family in order to satisfy her mother's desire for grandchildren before her biological clock ran out was not even worth considering. After years of grafting for a company that did not appreciate her and continually got her name wrong, she was going to rent a property and write the book she had longed to write ever since she was a child.

The cottage was everything she hoped it would be. Her last-minute fears that she had been scammed vanished upon her arrival when she saw the requisite roses growing around the front door, despite the lateness of the season; they would have made any chocolate box designer proud. The pale cream building was cocooned from the modern world, hidden at the edge of the Yorkshire village behind a stone wall. There was no drone of passing traffic, just the chatter of sparrows in the hedgerow and the gentle buzz of lazy bees gathering last-minute nectar before the cold weather arrived. The low sun shone on the honey-streaked hay in the thick thatched roof that covered the cottage like a cozy blanket. Only Tobias' yowl from his carry case alerted her that this wasn't a dream. The risk of using her redundancy money to rent somewhere in the sticks away from distraction had paid off. Rowan Cottage was hers to watch the late summer drift into Autumn, Winter, and Spring. When she left, her debut novel would be written, ready to submit, and she would be ready to start her new life as a fledgling author. Except she was failing at the first hurdle. A novel consisted of more than empty pages on a screen. Coffee, she needed coffee.

The kitchen was the oldest part of the rambling building, according to the introduction pack left with a welcoming box of local delicacies, and apart from the study, her favorite room. The traditional range and weathered farmhouse table added to its antiquity and cozy atmosphere. Tobias stretched his long black feline body in the patch of warm September sun. How many feet had walked across the worn flagstones or stood at the leaded windows, like her, looking at the garden and dramatic Yorkshire Moors beyond? Late-blooming flowers provided a splash of color, and a winding path led past an extensive herb garden full of plants she could not identify. Luckily, all she had to do was enjoy the scenery as the landlady assured her a gardener would pop over to keep an eye on things. Turbulent gray clouds threatened to replace the golden glow on the heathland. It was an everchanging masterpiece.

Come on, Emma, if that landscape does not inspire you to tell a story, you may as well pack your bags. She shook her head. She may be the flake, but the family stubbornness ran through her veins, and she would rather die than admit defeat. Her back straightened; she just needed a story.

Clutching her favorite mug, she inhaled the warm, bitter aroma of coffee and closed her eyes. Heaven.

Crash.

The kitchen door blew open and slammed against the wall. A blast of cold air curled around Emma as she jumped, sloshing the dark nectar to the floor. What the hell? Tobias fled the room and escaped to the garden. She cursed and called after him, knowing it was futile. He had been cooped in the house since their arrival. She only hoped he would return before the weather changed. What had happened? The incoming storm still lingered at the edges, and the air remained still.

"Tell mine," a faint whisper said close to her ear. She spun around. There was no one there. Pulling her cardigan around her and rubbing her arms, she checked again, poking her head outside. Emma was alone. She closed the door.

"Just a freak gust of wind," she muttered, mopping up the spilled coffee, "and a dose of overactive imagination." Through the window, Emma tracked Tobias's movement and smiled as he found another patch of sunlit ground to sleep on. Thank heavens he was as lackadaisical as she was. Bringing her mug to her lips, Emma took a sip and spat it out. It was freezing cold. Had time sped by without her realizing? It would not be the first time daydreaming had distracted her. But the clock disagreed, declaring only minutes had passed. Maybe she forgot to boil the water. Concentrating this time, she made a fresh brew.

•

Night fell early as the storm raged outside, the rain hammering on the windows as they rattled in the howling wind. With Tobias asleep on the rug in front of the fire, Emma curled up on an armchair with her fresh notebook and wine close to hand. She watched the orange flames rise and fall in their hypnotic dance, feeling her muscles relax. After a few sips of wine, the tension of the day seeped away. Her heavy eyes closed, and her breathing slowed as the sound of the crackling fire lulled her into a deep sleep. Immersed in the technicolor visions of her dreams, she leaned into a hand cupping her face. Goosebumps rose on her arm as a trail of ice ran up her body. A light breath caressed her neck, and a deep voice whispered in her ear. "Tell mine."

Tobias' sharp hiss and frantic scrambling across the parquet floor jolted Emma awake with a gasp. He stood with his hackles raised, glaring at her with wide eyes. He refused to be placated, forcing Emma to ease herself from her comfortable position to release him to the rest of the house. What was up with him? Storms never bothered him before. She shuddered with the recent cold, which the roaring fire failed to reach. A glance at the curtains surprised her. They had not moved in the breeze. Pulling her cardigan tight around her, she sunk back into the chair and tried to hold on to the snatches of dreams lingering on the edge of her consciousness.

Emma felt pressure on her shoulder, as if a hand had grasped it. "Tell the story of Charles Denver."

Charles Denver . . . Emma rolled the name she recognized from her dream around in her mind; it could work. She said it out loud as she scribbled it down, "Charles Denver." Mr. Charles Denver. No, Lord Charles Denver. A sweet intoxicating aroma of bergamot, citrus, and pipe tobacco filled the room and pulled her back into a dreamlike state. Within minutes, the words flowed, and her hand raced across the page to document the vibrant scenes racing through her mind. Hours passed, and her fist ached as it clutched the pen tight, trying to keep up with the speed of the creativity. Coming here was not a mistake; she had her story, and it demanded to be written.

•

Emma swallowed some painkillers and yawned. Despite sleeping in, her head pounded, and the remnants of her vivid dreams lingered. With a coffee in hand, she picked up her discarded notebook on the rug near the hearth. She began to read the unfamiliar frantic scrawl and scrunched up her nose. Had she really written this? Her last solid memory was sitting near the fire, listening to the storm, and Tobias's strange behavior. The rest was lost in a fragmented haze. She must have drunk more wine than she thought. Historical fiction was not the genre she had planned to write. The research needed to make it an accurate portrayal of the time would be a nightmare. She knew nothing about Victorian England. Readers would notice her lack of expertise and likely flag each mistake on their reviews. She shuddered; sometimes they could be brutal. And then there was Charles. His aristocratic views, judgemental stance, and snippy voice leapt from the pages she was reading. Emma screwed her nose up; he was not the protagonist she would read about by choice, never mind write. She wanted to write a romcom like the ones she loved, with an uplifting happi-ly-ever-after. No one, bar the buxom local seamstress and his wife Catherine, a sharp-featured woman who took her role as the Lady of the Manor seriously, could fall in love with Charles Denver. No, his story was not the one for her.

With the sun streaming through the study window and warming her back, she opened her laptop; contemporary romance was the way to go. Maybe even set in a small Yorkshire village with her heroine searching for new beginnings, like herself. Emma became immersed in brainstorming her new protagonist's world and woes, becoming unaware of her surroundings. Like the word that teeters on the edge of the tongue, the hook for the book was right in sight, ready to be grasped and—

An excited yap whipped her back into reality. The idea flitted away with the curse words she uttered. Scowling, she turned to the window, and her anger at the intrusion melted away. A man had entered the garden, laden with gardening tools and joined by an aged Jack Russell, padding at his side. Emma slipped into the shadows of the long and heavy, velvet curtains, not wanting to be caught staring. She studied his mannerisms as he weeded flower beds, noting the way he ran his fingers through his sun-bleached hair and how his dazzling smile reached his eyes when he called for the Jack Russell to come. The small details fired her imagina-tion. After a while, he stood and wiped his brow with his t-shirt, revealing his taut, tanned stomach, making her own flutter. Like her, readers would long to kiss his mouth and be wrapped in his muscular arms. Forget Charles Denver, she had found the perfect partner for her protagonist. She stepped closer to the window, eager to get a better look, but her stomach growled, reminding her she had missed breakfast. Armed with the perfect excuse, Emma decided to discover more about her novel's love interest. After all, it would be rude to make coffee and food for one.

•

Emma returned to her laptop buoyed with enthusiasm and caffeine. Not only was she inspired to write, she also had a date with Jez, the gardener. Maybe Chalky, his grandfather's dog, would come too as they seemed inseparable. They had chatted over their belated breakfast—a mountain of toast, coffee for her, and strong tea with two sugars for him—until Jez declared it was time to go back to work. She had readily agreed. Blending the information she gleaned from Jez into her work increased her word count, and she relished the warm tingle of excitement it gave. This was why she loved writing: the buzz, the escapism, the discovery of new characters. How could her characters meet? What obstacles could they face? The options were endless. Tobias snuck onto her knee while she typed, and his contented purr matched her mood for several hours until a cool draught whipped around her ankles. Tobias shot out of the room. "Tell my story."

"No, Charles. I won't," she said, grasping the female protagonist's image so it did not flitter away with the distraction. Did all writers get this—a character so alive and insistent that it's their turn for a story, despite the author's reluctance? "I don't even know what you look like."

The instantaneous change in atmosphere made Emma regret her words. Time paused as if it were waiting for what would happen next. The ceiling light flickered on and off multiple times, and the laptop screen went blank. "No," she screamed, "no, no, no." Had she pressed save? She frantically attempted to switch the machine on again, but it refused to fire up.

The temperature in the room plummeted.

"You do now." The clipped, demanding accent she recalled from the night before filled the room. In the winged arm-chair closest to the fireplace sat Charles Denver. His short dark hair, straight back, and crisp suit showed he was as arrogant as she'd imagined while reading the words from the previous night. He ignored her reluctance to engage with him and began to tell his story from where her previous notes ended. When he talked, he twirled the ends of his sleek, dark mustache with his fingers.

Charles was not the hero of a novel, Emma decided, until he spoke of her—his Sarah. His fierce gray eyes shone with joy, and warmth dispelled the sternness from his angular face with the mention of her name. Mesmerized, Emma picked up her notebook and began to write.

"I first saw her on the night of the Christmas ball. An idiotic maid had damaged Catherine's gown, and Sarah was summoned. Catherine would trust no one else to repair it. My wife may have been the one draped in expensive jewels and clothing, but it was Sarah who made the room shine."

His words provoked vivid images, captivating Emma as he described escorting Catherine down the sweeping staircase, past the magnificent Christmas tree and into the ballroom, bursting with swirling ballgowns and live orchestral music. He danced with his wife in his arms, but Charles's thoughts were with Sarah.

Time flew by, and Emma's date with Jez was forgotten as she continued to scribe Charles's story into the night. Days blurred into each other with minimal sleep. All that mattered was telling the story. It was a compulsion, an addiction to knowing more. Her heart warmed to Charles when she saw the passion between the lovers on chance meetings, and then whenever the opportunity arose for them to sneak away—a horse ride into the Moors, and a stay in Sarah's humble cottage when Lady Catherine visited her sister. His haughtiness slipped when Sarah fell ill, and his caring side showed with his attempt to make a simple broth to encourage healing. Emma admired his determination to do things for himself rather than smuggle some away from the manor's kitchen, and her heart ached when she experienced Charles's angst at being trapped in a loveless marriage of convenience while Sarah lived close by.

They slipped into a routine; as soon as the heady aroma of tobacco and distinctive cologne filled the room, Tobias would slink out and Emma would retrieve one of her notebooks, ready to write. Her laptop remained temperamental, the screen freezing or going black whenever inspiration for Charles's story struck. Writing by hand was more reliable, and the words materialized effortlessly every time he sat in the chair recalling his life, swirling the tumbler of his favored whisky or smoking his pipe.

Scenes unfolded before her while she listened to Charles. He painted the settings with his words, and she could see the dark wood panel in the parlor and the blazing fire in the large stone hearth. Two regal, willowy whippets laid alert beside Lady Catherine, her tight blond bun emphasizing her sharp features and beaky nose. She looked directly at Charles as he lumbered in, bedraggled from a storm. Emma gulped at the intense stare. She felt as though she had seen the piercing blue eyes before. They cut into the soul with an icy anger, scrutinizing their recipient and freezing them in explosive wrath.

"No," Charles's voice boomed. Emma jumped, and the image dissipated. "You have written it wrong. She wore blue, not jade. Her dress was periwinkle blue, the same as the day we first met. Oh, how bewitched I was! I saw eyes full with the promise of happiness and love. Once I gave her what she wanted, an heir, they became full of hate and contempt." Charles stood behind her, crushing her shoulders with his hands. "Details, however small, must be correct." Only when she crossed out her words and corrected the scene to his specifications did he release his unbearable grip and continue the tale.

Unnerved by the earlier experience, Emma strode out of the cottage and headed into the village. What had happened? She needed air. She needed space. How long had she been holed up in Rowan Cottage consumed by the story? Summer had morphed into Autumn and was now hurtling toward the chills of winter. Golden, red, and brown leaves laid scattered on the paths, while skeletal trees and hedgerows stood bare. In the High Street, pumpkins shone in windows as the retailers capitalized on the upcoming season. The bitter air bit through the fogginess and pressure in her head, relieving the headache that had plagued her for days.

Emma inspected the busy bakery's window, pondering which delight called for her more. The lemon drizzle cake promised to excite the taste buds with an explosion of tangy citrus, but the chocolate cake with its excessive decorations of chocolate buttons and Maltesers was equally tempting.

"Personally, I'd go for the custard slices, simple but never forgotten once tasted," Jez said, walking up to her. He was dressed in work clothes and had a streak of mud across his cheek, which Emma longed to wipe away. Chalky nudged her leg for attention, his tail wagging excessively. Heat rose to Emma's cheeks. She had not seen him since they'd arranged the forgotten date, and this confrontation was unavoidable.

"That's good to know," she finally stuttered.

"You stood me up." He continued, "It's fine, it wasn't the first time."

"Oh, Jez, I didn't mean to. I got caught up in my writing, and I couldn't find your number to apologize. And . . . "

"Really, I said it's fine," Jez said smiling, "but if you're free now, maybe we could grab some lunch? The Old Ram does excellent pies and they let Chalky in. When was the last time you ate?" Emma vaguely recalled shunning food preparation the night before in favor of listening to Charles. Her stomach rumbled in anticipation for something more substantial than toast. Company and good food were just what she needed.

The warm fragrance of hops, a roaring fire, and a bellowing laugh from the large man behind the bar welcomed her as they entered The Old Ram. Jez found a table, and Emma sat in the chair opposite him and stared at his eyes. They were similar to Lady Catherine's but still different. The hustle and bustle in the room provided a low background hum, and together with Jez's chat was a welcome distraction from her aching shoulders and growing unease. The waitress brought over their meals, and the smell of home-cooked pie spiked Emma's appetite. She tucked in, thankful it tasted as good as Jez promised it would.

"So what have you been up to?" Jez said.

Emma fiddled with her paper serviette and considered lying about her reason for staying at Rowan Cottage, but she remembered the advice in the writing chat groups: if she didn't believe she was a writer, others wouldn't either. Taking a deep breath, she said, "I'm writing a book." Emma waited for a sneer—or worse, laughter—but Jez leaned forward, urging her to continue.

"I was offered redundancy from a job I hated and decided to take the opportunity to write the novel I always promised I'd do."

"Well, that explains the new gaunt look. I see you huddled over your desk in the study when I come to tend the garden. My sister Milly is the same when she paints; creativity takes over, and she goes into another world no one can reach," said Jez.

Emma nodded. That was it, that was what she was experiencing, just intense creativity.

"What's it about?" Jez said, laying his cutlery down on his empty plate.

"Charles Denver and his complex love life." Emma gave him a concise version of the love triangle between Charles, his terrifying wife, and his true love and mistress, Sarah. Jez paled and took a swift drink from his beer.

"I didn't put you down as a history buff."

"I'm not. It wasn't what I was expecting to write. I read more contemporary books and thought I'd do something similar, but this story seemed to write itself."

"In what way?" Jez said as he studied her, allowing Emma the opportunity to gaze into his familiar eyes.

"The story is just there. I zone out, and the words flow onto the page; it's weird."

"Isn't that how you always write?" he said.

"No way," Emma shook her head and paused, noting how his relaxed posture had stiffened as he rubbed the back of his neck nervously. Had she said something wrong? "Apart from the occasional sparks of inspiration, every sentence is usually a slog. The house must be my muse."

"The house is definitely something. Say, why don't we go for a walk? Chalky will appreciate it." Jez called the dog from under the table, stood up, and grabbed her hand. "There's something you should see."

They walked through the village, Jez pointing out places and giving her a potted history, including the large manor on the hill. She did a double-take when she saw it as it resembled the place Sarah went to the ball, and again at the woodland that was similar to the place her characters picnicked. How could her imagination conjure up real places with accuracy? Jez unclipped Chalky's lead when they arrived at the church on the hill, and the dog disappeared from view into the graveyard. "He knows where to go," Jez said. They came to the edge of the graveyard where old lichen and moss-covered gravestones stood in disrepair. Chalky yapped from over a crumbling stone wall. Jez helped Emma over, and to her surprise, there was another gravestone hidden beneath brambles.

"What's this?"

"This is non-consecrated ground. The place where the villagers buried non-believers and those not worthy of being buried with the others. Meet my great-great-grandfather."

Jez carefully pulled back the brambles, and Emma peered at the gravestone for a closer look.

Here Lies Charles Denver

Lord Mexenby

4th January 1863 -5th October 1901

Emma recoiled from the grave, put her hand to her chest, and stared at Jez.

"But . . . " Words failed her. This could not be happening. Jez guided her to lean against the wall, her pale face reflecting the nausea and dizziness she felt. Charles Denver was real. Jez knew who her fictional character was. A multitude of questions spun in her mind as she tried to make sense of it all "I don't understand."

"You aren't the first to experience something strange at Rowan Cottage. It has a certain reputation around here, but not one they advertise. People have heard a woman singing in the garden and seen a man standing in the study. But you're the first to talk to him and hear his story."

Emma rubbed her shoulder, sore from Charles's recent grasp, took a deep breath, and stumbled back to the gravestone. She traced his green weather-worn name with her fingers. Charles was real. Not a figment of her imagination or someone she'd conjured up from her dreams. He had lived and died. She quickly calculated his age—he was too young to die naturally. "How? And why here, not with the others?" Emma pointed to the stones over the wall.

"Well, this is where the romantic fairy tale you're writing turns dark, much darker than you're expecting. Charles ended his affair with Sarah because he knew Catherine was suspicious." Jez held out his hand and led her into the churchyard to another grave. "Sarah was heartbroken and begged him to reconsider. Some say she threatened to tell Catherine the truth, but whatever the trigger, he flew at her in a fit of rage with fatal results."

Emma walked back to Rowan Cottage in stunned silence, grateful for Jez who continued to hold her arm, reassuring her as he guided her home. When they reached the gate, they stood silently, staring at the quiet cottage in its idyllic setting, hiding its horrific secret.

Finally, Jed broke the silence, "Are you sure you don't want me to come with you?"

"No need, I'll be quick. There's nothing to be scared of."

•

Emma stood in the doorway. All was calm, but she regretted declining Jez's offer. She longed for him to be by her side again. Any courage she'd felt drained away with every footstep down the garden path.

Breathe.

All she had to do was grab a bagful of clothes, Tobias, and his crate, then return to the comfort of the Old Ram where she could stay the night. She would not spend another night sharing a home with a murderer, dead or alive.

"Toby, Tobias," she called, shaking his favorite biscuits. He was nowhere to be seen as she climbed up the rickety stairs to her bedroom. Flinging clothes in her bag, she called again. "Come on, Toby. We need to leave."

"No!" The bedroom door slammed. The distinct smell of his tobacco surrounded her, and fronds of frost grew on the window panes like icy skeletons of leaves. Emma watched clouds form from her breath, paralyzed. She gulped.

"I need to tell my story."

Anger boiled inside her and broke through the shackles of fear holding her in place. "No, you're a murderer. For all the talk of how much you loved Sarah, you killed her. In cold blood."

"No. I did not do it. I loved her."

Had Jez lied to her about Sarah's murder? Had he gotten it wrong? Charles Denver loomed in front of her with his hands raised.

Fury flashed across his face. "I did not do it." He repeated, stepping forward and forcing Emma to back away until he trapped her against the wall. He clutched her arms, pinning her down. "I. Did. Not. Kill. Her."

Emma watched helplessly as scenes formed in front of her. She felt the thud of the hooves on the dry, cracked road and the rapid beat of Charles' racing heart as he urged the creature to go faster. Faster. Dust kicked up from the horse, tickling her throat and stinging her eyes. The landscape passed in a purple blur, and Emma could feel the blistering heat on her back. The stablehand's pale stricken face told Charles all he needed to know when he arrived back at the hall. Somehow Catherine had discovered his affair. How? It did not matter. He had to get to Sarah before she faced the wrath of his wife.

The garden gate hung open, and the front door stood ajar. Charles called his lover's name, racing through the cottage in rooms Emma recognized: her bedroom, the flagstones in the kitchen, and the familiar outlook across the moors. The house remained silent as if it held its breath, waiting for what was to come. An icy dread grabbed his heart when he saw the abandoned basket and scattered roses on the lawn through the kitchen window. He screamed her name and heard a faint groan in return. His Sarah. Her alabaster white skin and blood seeping on the path—a porcelain doll, broken. Her gardening scissors laid close by, smeared with blood. Charles ripped strips of fabric from her dress to hold against the wound on her side and stem the flow, then cradled her.

"I'm sorry. I'm sorry," he repeated over and over as her eyes fluttered and she took her final breath. The shrill police whistle filled the air, followed by the stampede of boots. He fought against the rough hands pulling him away from Sarah's limp body; he needed to stay with her. A kick connected with one officer, but others overpowered him. Movement at the bottom of the garden caught his eye as they dragged him away. Under the canopy of the trees, he swore he saw a woman dressed in black with glacial blue eyes. But he blinked and she was gone—only shadows remained.

Emma wiped the tears from her face, feeling his pain of losing the one he loved and the numbness of walking to the gallows. Charles released her, his solid form fading to a wisp but hovering close by. Emotionally and physically drained, she slumped to the floor and pulled a notebook toward her, concluding the story in her own shaky handwriting. Dusk fell, and the last remnants of Charles disappeared, warming the air and lifting the oppressive atmosphere with the words "The End."

•

Emma scribed her name with a flourish and handed the book over to the gentleman with a smile. He thanked her and stepped aside for the next person in line. She scanned the room and could not believe that the queue of people snaking through the bookshop were waiting for her. Sitting at the table with a pen poised to sign copies of her debut novel was a dream come true, but she struggled to comprehend that the best-selling novel based on a century-old miscarriage of justice was hers. With the help from Jez's grandfather, who hoarded papers and photos relating to his family history, and the discovery of Catherine's scandalous, anger-filled diaries in the attic, Emma could back up her claim that Charles was a victim of an avenging, twisted wife. A rumor started in the Old Ram, suggesting a stay in a haunted house inspired her, which only added to the intrigue and sales. The last year had been a whirlwind of agents, editors, and publishers. Being an author was more complicated than she ever expected, but Jez kept her going with pep talks and coffee to keep her awake for the endless edits. So much had changed thanks to Charles, including her love life. She grinned at the diamond ring glistening on her left hand.

Emma handed a signed copy to the next customer.

"What is your next book about?"

"I'm currently writing something light-hearted and—" A gentle, icy hand squeezed her shoulder, and a faint fragrance of jasmine intensified as a quiet female voice whispered, "Tell mine."

ABASIAMA UDOM

A Touch Of Gentle Madness

POETRY

Writer, poet, and polymath **ABASIAMA UDOM** was born in the rough areas of a Port Harcourt waterfront to a noisy Nigerian family. She believes this is what has helped shape her life, interests, and love for pidgin English, noisy conversations, and the abstract.

After a crazy experience with failure, she picked up writing from where she had dumped it. Pouring her thoughts into one poem which she wrote for two years that never saw the light of day.

Abasiama has published two short stories, "Pose" and "Coloured Tales," and other works featured in *Kalahari Review*, *Imspired*, *Rigorous Magazine*, and *Sandy River Review*.

Kikikiki, the pen drums across my teeth;
it is the next line that I seek.
Somehow the miscreant escapes my grasp,
slipping through as he mocks—
"Write na, you call yourself a writer: write."
I slap the chair, my lap, my face
none of it woos the words near.
I sit here muttering and I know:
a touch of gentle madness,
this is the writer's curse.

CAROL CASEY

Writing Cats And Dogs

POETRY

CAROL CASEY was born (1955) in Toronto, Ontario Canada. Her first major, literary event occurred when her grade eight teacher read her poems out loud to the class. This empowered her to think of herself as a poet for the rest of her life. Carol dropped out of high school to follow the pied-piper clarion call of the 1970s counter-culture movement. She gave birth to her first child in an alternative community called The Farm, in Tennessee, USA. She only got a lecture at the border upon returning to Canada when she answered the question, *Do you have something to declare that you acquired during your visit?*, by pointing to her infant son.

Motherhood, relationships, and career issues kept poetry at bay for some years. After her first marriage fell apart, she slowly wrote herself back together and found herself with a pile of poems, two bachelor's degrees, three marvelous children, two amazing stepdaughters, three wonderful grandsons, and a goddess-worshipping, gracefully aging hippie for a partner in Blyth, Ontario, surrounded by a large garden, fourteen chickens, and a thousand books. Carol is a longstanding member of the Huron Poetry Collective and an associate member of the League of Canadian Poets. Nominated for the Pushcart Prize by *The Prairie Journal* in 2017, she has been published in around fifty different anthologies and journals. One mentor described her work as having "a very natural musicality . . . an enchanting quality and authenticity that is rare." Her life makes most sense when she's dancing, and also, often, when she's writing poetry. Sometimes she gets the two confused.

There is a fear that pops up
just before I start to write.
It's like the dread that followed
me to swimming lessons as a child
a small, somewhat fuzzy stray dog
of a trepidation; friendly enough
but with a hint of kismet.
It sidled up to the edge of the pool
just before I jumped,
vanished at the teacher's command.

It's gone now that I've started writing,
tail vanishing between legs.
I fancy that if I let it in the door,
it would grow as big as my house,
break my pen, and sit on my hand
till I'd have to move out
or splinter the rafters.

By the way, this not bringing
the dog home is a cat I found in an alley,
a large, unruly, battle-scarred tom;
scary enough, but with a hint of cadence, that
purrs at my feet as I write,
rubs against my legs,
hisses when it sees the dog.
I feed him scraps
and continue writing.

DAVID JESSON

Today, I Will Write

FICTION

"This may be the only book you ever write—make sure you're proud of it!" was the advice given to DAVID JESSON when he was writing his thesis. Since then, he's tried to make sure that he is proud of everything he writes. As a professional scientist and engineer, David is used to writing with others and is the co-author of more than thirty academic papers. This has bled over into his creative writing: with his writing partner he shares a blog, Fiction Can Be Fun, and together they've just completed *The November Deadline*, the first book in The Echo Sanction, an urban fantasy/thriller series, which starts in the bombed out docklands of London shortly after the end of the Second World War. David has previously published short stories in *Kyanite* and the *Crux Anthology*, and has an essay in *The Secret Science of Superheroes*.

Sunlight edged through the crack in the curtains. Inch by inch, it crept toward my face, ensuring that, when it reached my eyes, I woke up in a blind panic. My body went from horizontal to vertical in under a second, autonomic functions informing me that I was late. Guilt sloshed through me: how could this have happened?

My heart rate subsided as my brain caught up. I squashed the angst about being tardy for work; I'd booked the day "off!" A rare and cherished day of annual leave, beginning with an equally infrequent, and until a moment ago, very enjoyable lie-in. The day was to be a writing day. The garden needed work, the house needed work, work needed work, but writing time was precious, to be savored and enjoyed.

But first, breakfast and a cup of tea. I could feel the bags under my eyes receding as I sipped my cuppa, thinking about the project I would work on today. With the necessities out of the way, I settled myself down with a notebook and my favorite fountain pen. Go words, go!

Nothing.

Ah! Of course! A day of annual leave called for the good stuff. I bustled 'round the kitchen, channeling TV ads from the 80s and making the noise of a percolator as coffee brewed in the cafetiere. Whilst the magic happened, I emptied the dishwasher, thought about what to make for supper, rearranged the cutlery drawer, and—there was a knock at the door. Very inconvenient. Just as I was about to press the plunger down on the coffee too.

How exciting! It was the postman with a parcel—an unexpected pleasure! The address label was inside one of those little plastic wallets, which made me wonder if there was an invoice. I removed it and unfolded the paper inside.

Dear writer,

We are huge fans of the work you've presented on Twitter and have thus selected you as the recipient of the DreamWriter! You are under no obligation to trial this demonstration model of our new writers-aide, but

*we trust that if you do use the device, you will offer
an honest review.*

*Kind regards,
Team DreamWriter*

Weird. I mean, my Twitter game is strong, but I don't really
have *that* many followers. Anyway, what's in the box? I am notorious
for opening Christmas presents in the shortest time possible. As I
contemplated ripping the box open, it occurred to me that I might
need to return whatever was inside. So I opened the box carefully,
only to find a smaller box held in place by a polystyrene cage. The
smaller box was about the size of one that would hold a cycling
helmet, and the garish packaging seemed to be indicating that this
was exactly what was inside: a helmet called the DreamWriter. I
did not need a new cycling helmet.

I put the box on the hall table and returned to my notebook.
For about a minute. Then I returned to the hall and opened the
lurid inner box to find out about the DreamWriter. It really did
look like a cycling helmet, but with two leads, both ending in USB
ports. I read the instructions. I read them again. I read them a third
time because I couldn't believe what I was reading. A writer could
simply think about what they wanted to write, and the Dream-
Writer would do all the hard work of actually putting the thoughts
into words. There were some training and calibration steps so that
the DreamWriter could attune itself to the writer's thoughts and
writing style, but, the blurb promised, productivity would increase
dramatically as soon as these steps were completed.

OK.

Why not?

I checked the doohickey over. Yep, I could see where electrodes
were mounted, but there were no signs they would actually enter
my skull or anything. There didn't appear to be a reservoir for
some kind of gunk—bio or nano or whatever—that would take
over as soon as I plugged the thing in.

I'm not a big fan of horror films, so there was only a tiny
"don't go in the haunted house" tingle. But still . . . caution. I

would give this a go, but not on a device that held any personal data, just in case. I had an old PC that I was rebuilding for fun: I cleared away the clutter and fired the electronic skeleton up. I got my coffee whilst it was thinking, then loaded the software and plugged in the leads.

Deep breath.

I put the helmet on, tightening the chin strap that held it in place. Even before I'd finished adjusting it, text began to appear on the screen. To begin with, it was just gibberish, but with each exercise completed, the text began to clear. Full sentences emerged from a sea of random characters. At first, they were simple check-phrases: "The quick brown fox jumped over the lazy dog." Before long, though, sentences that I recognized as my style started building into paragraphs and scenes—a story.

I took a sip of coffee. Amazing! The coffee was still the perfect temperature—unheard of when I was in the throes of writing, usually. I wrote some more, tried a few different techniques, and enjoyed my coffee. When there was nothing left but grounds, I took the helmet off, went to the kitchen, and refilled my mug, my mind whirling with possibilities. Would the DreamWriter also work for illustrations? First things first, though: there were a couple of other ideas that had been floating around in my brain recently, and I would get these out and onto paper today, too. It would be my most productive writing session ever.

Helmet donned, I settled down. This time, there was no cal-ibration process; it immediately strung together the words from my subconscious. Again, the words appeared so fast the screen became a blur. I put the words "The End" to a novel. This was the first time that I had written those words on a project of this length. I felt lightheaded from the elation of success, like an athlete who has broken not only a personal best but a world record too. The possibilities were dizzying; perhaps I could afford to give up my job and focus on writing?

A plot rose to the surface of my mind from the bubbling depths where it had been taking form for weeks, and I started on another project. Something didn't feel right, though. I checked back on what was being written.

"Mary had a little lamb . . . "

This was not my project.

"It was the best of times, it was the worst of times . . . "

Was it possible to spend too long working with the Dream-Writer?

"In a hole in the ground . . . "

There hadn't been a warning label, had there? Had I missed it in my excitement?

"it Woz A darK & sturmey nicht . . . "

Definitely weird. Don't fail me, DreamWriter!

Now completely blank, the screen flickered through a cycle of nausea-inducing colors. I felt a migraine coming on. I checked the fit—all OK. I checked the connections—all firm. An alarm began to sound. What was going wrong? I took the helmet off and looked over it again—there must be something loose . . . I'd give Team DreamWriter a review, all right. One star!

My attention moved from the leads to the helmet itself, but somehow I couldn't focus on it. It was fuzzy, lacking in detail, almost as if it were evaporating.

Noooo! I let out a groan and raised my head from the pillow. There was no pleasant sunshine on my face. Outside, it was still dark. No day of annual leave; the day job beckoned. Anguish overwhelmed me, a dark wave dragging me under. No Dream-Writer. I would have to write my story the old-fashioned way, word by laborious word.

I reached for a notepad and started to scribble.

SHANE SCHICK

Super Ars Poetica

POETRY

SHANE SCHICK (b. 1973) was born and raised in a small town in Ontario, Canada. He studied journalism in Toronto, and after a brief stint at the *Toronto Star*, he joined a group of technology publications, eventually becoming the first online editor, spearheading the company's move into digital media. He then became a weekly columnist for Canada's *The Globe and Mail*.

At 31, Schick received an award from the Canadian Advanced Technology Alliance (CATA), which said, "Shane exemplifies journalistic integrity and finely honed news judgment . . . his keen intelligence and engaging writing style results in analytical, investigative stories that examine the trends, products, and people impacting the Canadian technology industry."

Schick later expanded beyond the world of technology to cover the ad industry as Editor-in-Chief of *Marketing* magazine, and in 2020 launched his own publication about the emerging discipline of customer experience design, *360 Magazine*. Behind the scenes—always—was creative writing and poetry. "I always struggled to write poems that I felt were as strong as my work as a journalist," he says. "Then I started to read more poems through a journalist's eyes and realized they were also a kind of reporting. The difference was that instead of reporting the news, poems were reporting ideas, a state of mind or a moment that was in no way time-sensitive. Instead of practicing journalism and writing the so-called first draft of history, I could try to capture it in a way that could be relevant forever." Schick's poetry has been published in literary journals across the U.S., Canada, the U.K. and Africa.

Origin stories are really for caped crusaders,
people who can channel interplanetary chaos
into a career in public service, or who know how
to manipulate your Messiah complex into
cosplay for confronting injustice.

You don't master rhyme and meter more readily
after being bitten by a radioactive spider,
and skyrocketing into orbit as an infant
doesn't mean you'll craft stanzas stronger than steel.

The Poet is a secret identity, one so hidden
that tearing open your single-breasted suit
reveals only an emblem you've yet to draw,
a signal that can't shine into the night sky

to call for anyone's help, especially yours,
until you've finally figured out that
your newfound powers are largely confined
to filling in the thought bubbles above

everyone's heads with what might never
have come to mind otherwise, something
that may be regarded more as the act
of a vigilante than a hero, a person

unable to fly, but whose furtive way of
standing, walking, or sitting and staring out
the window all the time suggests
they're less than fully grounded, either.

CHRISTIANA DOUCETTE

Story Shells

POETRY

Born in South Carolina, CHRISTIANA DOUCETTE grew up in and around Ann Arbor, MI but was drawn back to the state of her birth by college, temperate temperatures, and her husband's second grad degree. A few years post graduation in Minnesota convinced her the sharp northern winds were not her friends, and she now happily resides just far enough from the ocean for several long weekends a year.

In a home where audiobooks played every time the family climbed in the car, and mornings began with her mother reading classics aloud over breakfast, Christiana couldn't help but love the craft of story. A degree in Speech Performance furthered her understanding of story and the way emotions and subtext shift the meanings of words.

After a minor flirtation with playwriting, Christiana found home in poetry and Middle Grade prose. During COVID, Opera Composer Mark Buller set her poem "Beneath the Pressure of Petals" into an art song for his *Quarantine Miniature #4*. Her writing has been described as " . . . lovely and lyrical," "vivid and gorgeous," and "haunting and beautiful." But might be best summed up as "moving."

Sometimes,
Fingertips only find fragments,
Broken clam shell words,
Dark half-sentence mussels
Crusted with barnacles
And adjectives.

But sometimes,
Before concerns pick the mind clean,
Or the crosscurrent of routine
catches and riptide responsibilities
Wash out wit on waves of doubt—

Search the blank shore
For well-worded whelks, and moon shell metaphors—
Sift free the shark teeth verbs camouflaged
In gerund and infinitive shards.

And,
When toes trip on shell tips
That don't give when pressed,
Drill down.
Fall to hands and knees and dig.
Let grit grind beneath the fingernails
And sting the eyes.

Embrace the wind shivering up your spine.
Ignore the surge licking your feet,
Pulling you back—
The shell
Is worth the trouble.

Brush back the sand,
And bits of other shells
Left by dark and stormy nights,
The broken story arcs and character clichés
Shrouding this story's shape.
Sentence sediment
Swirls loose between your hands
As you scoop,
But don't lose focus.
Keep hold of the shell.

Lift it free.
Wade back into the waves.
Check the structure for holes,
Rinse the debris free,
Brush grey away
'Til flashes of orange-red
Glow
Like a rising sun.

TONI WALL

Birthday Money

FICTION

TONI WALL (b. 1983) grew up in eastern Pennsylvania where she was homeschooled for the entirety of her elementary and high school education. She began writing at a very early age when the writers of her favorite television shows didn't always get it right. Toni wrote fan fiction before she knew what fan fiction was. And, indeed, she was shocked to find out that other people shared the hobby.

Fan fiction quickly morphed into original fiction, and Toni was applauded by numerous people during her college years on her ability to pen a narrative. Toni attended a theological college where she met her husband. They married the year she graduated, and after moving to Arkansas, Texas, and Oklahoma, she managed to drag him back to Pennsylvania where they live with their three sons.

Toni's dream was always to publish a book. Her debut novel, *Persuasion of Deceit* (September 2021), was quickly followed by a request from her publisher for the sequel. She is most comfortable when creating worlds and characters in a fantasy setting, a predilection that stems from her love of reading the same genre. Writing is therapy for Toni, and escaping into worlds of magic and intrigue is how she relaxes on a daily basis. Within Toni's work you'll find drama, love, and a healthy dose of angst—all of which will leave you questioning the outcomes and eager for another look. When she's not writing, Toni can be found chasing and/or feeding children and dogs, or with her attention firmly ensconced in yet another fantasy novel.

The small bell above the door of the bookstore jingled softly, announcing their arrival. The scent of freshly brewed coffee greeted them and drifted out into the chilly air, inviting anyone else who might be passing by to come into the warmth of the little shop.

There was no fancy café or barista, only a small coffee pot on a table in the back of the room with a hand-lettered sign inviting patrons to help themselves. Her mother always poured herself a cup, three sugars and three creams, to sip while the little girl browsed.

The little girl used to drag her mother there at least once, sometimes twice, a week. But she would later remember this day vividly. She had just turned eight years old, and the weight of the money she received as a gift sat heavily in the bottom of her little Raggedy Ann purse. "Burning a hole," her mother had said.

The little girl scanned the shelves, letting her fingers drift over the smooth spines. There were wizards and Olympians, mice and dragons, but none of them called out to her. She had already read most of them. Then she saw it.

The display was set up in the children's section, an entire rack of glossy spiral-bound notebooks in the brightest colors the girl had ever seen. There were pink and blue dolphins leaping towards a beach ball, a pair of snow leopards with rainbow spots, and a curious seal in front of a spray of colorful kelp. She had to have one.

She snatched a notebook off the shelf. "Mommy! This one! This one!"

Her mother looked down at the book the little girl held and smiled softly, "Sweetie, this is only a notebook. Only lined paper. Wouldn't you rather have a new story to read?"

"Mommy, look at the leopards." The little girl ran a small hand over the glossy cover. "They do have words! They're just not in the book yet. I can write them there."

The mother's smile widened at the little girl's fervor, "All right, it's your money." An excited squeak was the only reply.

The little girl placed the notebook on the counter, and the cashier looked up in surprise. "This isn't your usual choice."

"I got money for my birthday, and I'm going to buy this book and write a story."

"Well, you read enough, I'm sure you'll be able to write a wonderful story."

The little girl's wide blue eyes could barely see above the counter, but she watched carefully as the cashier rang up the notebook and placed it in a brown paper bag. He gave the little girl her total, and with reverence, the girl placed her money on the counter, exchanging it for the notebook with the rainbow spotted snow leopards.

When she saw that notebook on the shelf and heard those two snow leopards whisper, *tell our story*, she felt that story burning inside and couldn't refuse. She took the notebook home and wrote her first novel. When she wrote "THE END" in her sloppy eight-year-old handwriting and raced to her mother, begging her to read it, she knew she would write for the rest of her life. That was when she knew that nothing would ever give her such a satisfying sense of accomplishment and worth as creating whole worlds from her own heart.

She still has it. It sits on her shelf next to her other books. And sometimes, when writing starts to feel like work, she likes to pull it down and read it, and remember the passion that ignited within her that day in her favorite little bookstore.

ALESSANDOR EARNEST

POETRY

ALESSANDOR EARNEST (The Imp of Editing) is a developmental editor, writing coach, and wizard behind innumerable curtains, from M Theory Comics to the Writers of Strange Fiction Con.

Alessandor is often so busy with outrageous schemes and pursuits that writing occasionally takes the back burner. That said, expect to see a graphic novel of interconnected shorts that could get even Bill Murray excited about the Groundhog Day trope. It will be released . . . someday.

For now, there's the Writers of Strange Fiction Podcast, where Alessandor grills really impressive people about writing, editing, publishing, marketing, rulebreaking, and everything between.

To give you a glimpse of the madness behind the myth, author D. Jose Ayala offers this cheeky anecdote: "The human body is a blank canvas for those who don't mind needles. My left ass cheek features a portrait of the inimitable Alessandor, a token of our lifelong friendship."

Writing is a strange alchemical process:
Inspiration flows past unknown geography and faraway lands
Sometimes rushing, sometimes trickling
Through currents of insight and eddies of meaning
Over the falls of climax
Into the stillness of resolution
Carrying only the finest particles in her heart
To lay as a delicate mire in the shallows
Ready for the potter's touch.

Editing is a messy and intricate affair:
First, she massages and pounds and smooths out impurities
Before soliciting the help of the throwing wheel
To work the formless mass into shape
Revolving and revolving
A collaboration—symbiosis
Transforming what was once soft and malleable
Into a solid vessel of beauty and utility
To hold treasures, sustenance, perhaps a flower.

Reading is a transformational experience:
Every vase, bowl, and urn begins its journey as a mighty river
And ends it gathering dust on a shelf, a table
But do not be fooled by its seemingly sorry state—
Here it will begin its life anew
A treasured and revered objet de temps
That holds all of what is, was, and will be
Everything that's real to the dreamers and children
And everything that never was.

That's a book.

L. DACRE TYNAN

The World Beneath Books

NON-FICTION

L. DACRE TYNAN (b. circa 1980) has been defined (by himself no less) as the loudest introvert in the room, and if online personality tests are to be trusted, this benchmark of gorgeous juxtaposition is a highly accurate appraisal. L is the initial for Luke (Latin for *light*). The Tynan surname comes from an anglicized version of the Gaelic name "O Teimhneain," which is derived from the word "teimhean," meaning "dark." Hence his name literally means, '*light something** dark.' L. Dacre, thrives within the parameters of being a walking, talking, basketball-loving, coffee consuming contradiction. L. Dacre currently offers his services for the online literary journal *Five South* as an Associate Editor and is currently working on two novels.

*For those keeping score, Dacre means 'trickling stream.' Truly.

I remember precisely when and where it was, the time I found that secret place: Shelly Beach, Port Macquarie, Australia. I was eight, and I'd taken my swimming goggles with me. We had swum at Shelly Beach for years, for as long as I could recall growing up, but never with these goggles. They were strictly for the indoor pools only.

The feelings I experienced the day I snuck them to the beach, the day that I found the secret underwater world, are feelings I'll never let go of. The winding sandy troughs and shallow channels of rock were dressed with Neptune's necklace and pointy purple sea urchins, so dark they looked like clustered exclamations. I meandered mindfully as an invited guest to an underwater kingdom should, slowly paddling among the schools of bream and whiting zig-zagging just beyond reach, with families of scuttling sand crabs peeking out from their homes. A realization poured over me in the few hours we played at the beach that day: I could take these goggles, meant for the chlorinated Olympic-sized pools, and open up a world below the crashing waves and tides and sunlight—*the world below the water.*

I was a child in the middle of an epiphany, like a superhero realizing a hidden power. I would breathe deep, hold the air in my lungs, and drop below the water to traverse sandy roads and villages of rock and coral. I stayed there as long as I could, seeing it all, taking it all in. My lungs would burn, and the pressure would build until I would rise to the surface, gasping for air.

It's that feeling of coming up from below the surface, punching through and out to draw a breath, that has stayed with me, the feeling of having been down *there*, being present in a secret world, and experiencing as much as my little lungs, brain, and heart could accommodate at a time. And then going back for more, over and over.

Now forty, with those halcyon swimming days behind me, I've connected to that younger version of myself once again. I've found another world full of even more secrets, majesty, and inspiration. Secret worlds in words. Specifically, in the creation of a story, before it can be read or heard by others. The world between the page and the writer.

To recount: I was an avid reader from a young age, accustomed to the feeling only avid readers feel—you know the one—the sensation of being swept up and along in the tales of knights and superheroes, explorers of both space and sea. Of glorious adventure and far-off lands. Of friends, be they man or beast. Of the forces that impede and push the hero to succeed.

Like swimming through water, the place of books and their printed pages was equally immersive, something I knew well. But it wasn't the *through* that got me. It was the *beneath*: diving below the water with goggles on and finding for the first time, the secret place of the writer's world—*the world beneath books*.

Much like taking those swimming goggles to the beach all those years ago and having the world open up around and below me before coming into clear focus, I can recall my "underwater moment" vividly. I recount it for both our sakes' now.

My working week was filled with endless talking, and I regularly found solace in the quiet fortitude of the hallowed lunch break. I had a rule: these breaks would be set entirely for silence. (I made my speech therapist proud.) I would read often, and even more regularly, I would daydream about things of little consequence. But this particular day, I went swimming in my mind. I started to think of places, faces, and names: vague identities forming. A purpose, a hero's journey, and then a plausible roadblock!

I was taken aback: "I *think* I am thinking of a story."

Digging around for paper and a pen, I started jotting down some of these key elements as they circled, just out of reach at first, elusive like the sand crabs, scurrying about their rock and coral homes. But as I continued, a loose plot became sharper in my mind's eye. I could see an antagonistic force, a back-story, and subplots forming around and throughout. I wrote and wrote. I filled pages and pages, writing like a *madman* for forty minutes. Crashing under waves of incessant scribbling, my chicken salad was all but forgotten.

And that's when it happened: the moment that linked me back to the same emotional charge and "lost-breath" moment I experienced at the beach—I came up for air.

It was like breaching the water's surface to inhale deeply, to regain my breath. I had resurfaced to the noise and the hubbub of the food court. My lunch break had vanished, eaten up by my inspired scrawling, with line after line of crowded handwriting now laid out in front of me. Like a warm memory that sat close in my mind, just behind my eyes, the experience lingered in the tension of my writing hand and racing heart.

I wanted to jump up and laugh and high-five strangers and smile back at the girl who worked at Boost Juice (and had *obviously* seen me writing like a maniac, her rueful smile giving away her amused puzzlement). I had found the world beneath books. I had held my breath and explored it and had the rush that only a writer knows.

That first rush is different from the "first" of many things: the first time you hold your date's hand at the movies or get the courage to start up a conversation with your crush on the walk home from school or the first kiss that strikes at you like lightning.

The second and third time may feel right, but it's the electricity of feeling the *first* instance that is hard to replicate. But finding yourself in *the world beneath books?* This is the writers' rush we go back for again and again. It will always resonate and jolt and produce reverence, and it is always as true.

If I am ever chasing the motivation to write, I recount my underwater moment. I swim again, under the crystal clear waters of Shelly Beach, and see the fish and the urchins and the sand crabs. I hold onto that moment, holding my breath in time with the memory, and then I burst upwards, taking a lung full of air, readying myself for the rush to come.

The secret place is only a page, a paragraph, or even a sentence away. So dear fellow writer, take a moment and prepare yourself for the writing opportunities that lay just ahead. Take a deep breath and steady yourself before the blank page, knowing that you are about to experience something of perspective, purpose, and true clarity as you dive into *the world beneath books.*

SHER TING

Earthwork

POETRY

SHER TING grew up in Singapore before moving to Australia for medical school. Growing up, she used to spend hours in the library, falling in love with the way words fell together to build worlds, the way they spoke when words no longer sufficed. Even as she majored in science, she has never lost her love for literature. She was a finalist in *The New York Times* Asia-Pacific Writing Competition and has work published/forthcoming in literary magazines including *Eunoia Review*, *Opia Mag*, *Overheard*, *Capsule Stories*, and *Interstellar Lit*.

Her work speaks of themes of loneliness/loss and memory/nostalgia with an exploration of naturistic landscapes, particularly the ocean. She hopes that, through her work, she is able to shed light on experiences that others will be able to relate to. "My work is not just about the sun at the end of the tunnel, but the drive, the light, and the shadows in between. It is not just about coming home but about opening every door within." Sher Ting is currently an editor of the *Aurora Journal* and a poetry reader for *Farside Review*. When she is not writing, she can be found playing her guitar and seeking out a new adventure.

I drink the encroaching horizon at dusk,
breaking my body, tooth and nail,
into the crumbs of my words

My pen moves clockwise with time,
drawing ink from a river of living water,
an upstroke swimming through
the eddy of night

In the lurid whitewater rush,
my breath stills into the shape of a thought,
quivering at the embankment of gushing prose

My mind falls across escarpment and periphrasis
to breathe life into ivory sheets

Circumlocution and kennings hewn by the pen's silvered blade,
euphemisms entombed beneath water-blistered land

I wade waist-deep into a vowel meadow
to plough tributaries from a reservoir of unspoken verse,
sinking my trowel deep into the marrow of memory,

that, in the incandescent glow of castor and hemp,
my words shall unravel their shivering leavings,
spread their brambling thistles,
and catch the yolk of dawn.

KELLY ESPARZA

My Performance

NON-FICTION

KELLY ESPARZA was born and raised in California. She gravitated toward telling stories from a young age, dreaming of one day publishing. Kelly followed this passion by the inspiration by her family's advice: "Write from the heart." Starting as a novelist, Kelly soon branched out to writing poetry, creative nonfiction, and children's literature. She enjoys incorporating uplifting messages in her work and is interested in writing stories that allow for a social commentary.

In 2016, Kelly was the recipient of the Scholastic Art and Writing Gold Key Award for Short Fiction, the Scholastic Art and Writing Silver Key Award for Poetry, and the Scholastic Art and Writing Silver Key Award for Photography. She then attended the University of Arizona where she further developed her craft and graduated with a B.A. in English and a B.A. in Creative Writing.

In 2019, Kelly wrote and self-published her first collection of poetry and prose titled, *The World as Seen Through My Eyes*. She then collaborated with two other authors to co-write a children's book, *Out of This World!*, published on the Make Way for Books app as an e-book. A year later, Kelly's poems, personal essays, and short fiction stories found homes in various literary journals. Additionally, she became a freelance screenwriter and co-wrote a screenplay for a feature film. "Kelly's writing ranges from shorter, inspirational, and calming poetry and prose to longer and exciting page-turning novels," state her peers, "allowing for a strong voice to shine through." With so many interests, it's hard to predict where Kelly's writing will go next, though she hopes for a novel debut.

"Writing takes courage," Sandra Cisneros, the author of *The House on Mango Street*, said at a book signing I attended a year ago. She pointed out that writing causes authors to be vulnerable, but it's a gift to show emotion and to express ourselves, as this is what makes us human. I found this to be true. To me, writing was special and personal. It was a creative outlet that made me feel free, eliminating any anxiety I felt. Writing was like a dance performance where every piece was a graceful move, and writers consistently exposed their vulnerabilities. I keep Cisneros's words in my mind now as I continue to find my voice in my writing. I often think back to a time when writing allowed me to take a leap of faith.

•

I was sixteen, a sophomore to be precise, full of eagerness to take on the world. It was the annual September school club fair, and this was the year I would get involved. When I was comfortable in a certain situation, I could be outgoing, but when it came to introducing myself and the initial small talk, my anxiety had other plans for me. Although I tried to appear confident, I wasn't, and I often thought too much of what others thought of me. But this year would be different. I would no longer be a shy freshman. Determined to finally break out of my shell, I figured joining a school club would be a fun way for me to meet other like-minded people and to try something new. I was ready to welcome a new change into my life.

I stood by the stairs leading into the courtyard where everyone ate lunch. The sun's warmth soaked into my skin as a cool breeze hugged me from behind. The fair began at the edge of the freshly mowed grass and extended to the gym's entrance. I walked towards the commotion, a large crowd forming and surrounding the various tables that were staggered in a zigzag manner. I could see the tops of posters displayed on each table. Excited chatter from the students carried around the maze. Dipping in between the crowd of potential club joiners, feeling awkward in my own skin, I perused the different stands and posters. Newspaper club. Happiness club. Science club. Robotics. Nothing piqued my interest until I saw it, stopping me in my tracks. A teen girl around my age stood beside a table, handing out fliers. A poster on the table read, "New Literary Magazine—Join Today!" My eyes lit up with curiosity. At the time, I didn't know there was such a thing as a creative writing magazine.

"Would you be interested in joining?" the girl asked me. I met her gaze and nodded. "Please sign your name, and put your email here." She gestured to a clipboard on the table, a few names and emails already scribbled on the paper. I stepped up and picked up the pen attached to the clipboard, bending over the table to sign. When I straightened, the girl's blue eyes brightened and she grinned. "Perfect. I hope to see you at our first meeting in two weeks!" she said. I returned her smile and thanked her.

My chest tightened at the thought of attending a meeting where I wouldn't know anyone, and I'd have to introduce myself. I shook my head. I wasn't going to psych myself out as I had many times before; I refused to allow my anxiety to prevent me from trying something new—something that I knew could be beneficial for me. Placing myself out of my comfort zone was what I wanted, and besides, this was a club centered around writing, which was my passion. I was ready to embrace this new change, and little did I know, this was only the beginning of many more opportunities to come.

•

Two weeks went by in the blink of an eye, and I found myself standing outside the classroom where the meeting would be held. I was about fifteen minutes early. Taking a deep breath, I swung open the heavy door and walked inside. The editor-in-chief immediately recognized me and waved me over. She stuck out her hand to me and introduced herself as Zoey. I timidly shook her hand, then took a seat in the second row of desks. A few other girls were scattered around the room, quietly eating their lunches. Meanwhile, Zoey and two other girls stood in front of a large whiteboard, casually talking to each other while occasionally glancing at the clock, waiting for the meeting to begin. When it was time, they each took a step forward and introduced them-selves, telling us what role they played in creating this club and literary magazine.

"We wanted to create a space where students could freely express themselves in an artistic way. We were thinking of having 'Reflections' be our first issue's theme," Zoey continued. She then went on to describe how she hoped to incorporate a theme for each issue and to create the magazine in a digital format.

Immediately, I could feel the gears in my mind working, trying to think of a short story idea. Writing fiction was my first love; it was what I was the most comfortable with and always gravitated toward. What idea could I come up with to fit the "Reflections" theme, though? Would it be Young Adult? Maybe it would be science fiction or fantasy in some way. I wanted my writing to be special. After all, I could be making my dreams a reality—getting my work *published*, which had been my goal since I was a little kid.

After school that day, I told my mom about the literary magazine, how excited I was to participate, and how I was still trying to think of writing ideas. She knew of my goal to put myself out there more this year and encouraged me to submit in a different genre, suggesting poetry. I'd always enjoyed reading poems for English class, but this was the first time I'd considered ever writing some of my own. Up until this point, I'd only thought of myself as a fiction writer, but after some extra thought, I decided to take my mom's suggestion and submitted two reflection poems, one called "Wrath" and the other "Love."

•

About a month later, I received an email. "Congratulations," it said. "Your poems, 'Wrath' and 'Love,' were selected for the magazine." I sat back, my hazel eyes widening. I was surprised for two reasons. One, my work was getting *published*. Not to be a pessimist or anything, but I knew rejection was a major possibility; it was something that *every* writer faced. After all, I had never taken any creative writing classes before and knew there was always room for my writing to improve.

Two, poetry was different from anything I'd ever written. It could be short; it could be long. It wasn't the same as writing a short story or a novel. The poetic format and style felt awkward, and it came a little less naturally to me—or so I thought.

And yet, here I was, staring at my iPad screen, gazing at the "Congratulations" email in all its glory. I let out a small breath. It was then that I wondered that perhaps I needed to have more confidence in myself—that I was capable of writing in other genres besides fiction.

•

A few months later, I received another email. This time it was from my high school's administration. "Good afternoon," it said. "I read your poems, 'Wrath' and 'Love,' in the school magazine and loved them. In three weeks from today, there will be a special school assembly on the seven deadly sins, and we're looking for students in different clubs to participate. I'm hoping that you'll read your poems at the assembly for the 'Wrath' section. Please let me know. Thank you. Sincerely, Paul Roberts." My mouth opened, but no words came out. A rollercoaster of emotions swept through me as I tried to wrap my mind around the exciting news.

On one hand, what an honor! Wasn't this what I'd always wanted? Wasn't my overall goal as a writer to touch another person's heart? Wasn't it to inspire someone else? Of course it was. On the other hand, though, I would have to speak in front of the entire school. The student body totaled about a thousand people. I swallowed hard at the thought. Class presentations were already nerve-wracking, and if I struggled with initial introductions and small talk, how could I possibly speak in front of a thousand people? The question stuck in my throat. For me, writing was a silent escape, but here, I would have to speak my words out loud. Sure, since I was a kid, it was always my goal to get my writing published and be out there for the world to read. But reading my work aloud in front of a large group of people was an entirely different, terrifying act—one that I was unsure I was capable of doing. My thoughts played tug-of-war with my heart, leaving me torn about what to do.

•

With the added encouragement of my family, I swallowed my anxiety and decided I would do it. The idea and the fear of public speaking followed me around like a shadow, but instead of this bringing me down, it lit a fire underneath me to do what I would call impossible. This was a once-in-a-lifetime opportunity that I couldn't turn down. I also didn't want my fear to be the reason I decided not to participate, leaving me with the "what if" question, wondering what could've happened if I'd just tried. For the next few weeks, I practiced my poems over and over, paced back and forth in my room, the living room, all over my house. I recited my poems to my family several times. I kept practicing until I had both pieces memorized.

And then the day came—the day I was dreading and anticipating simultaneously. Anxiety formed as a lump in my throat, and my hands were clammy with sweat. I sat in the designated chairs by the podium, my legs trembling ever so slightly. I watched the sea of students emerge from the two heavy doors of the gymnasium, trudging up the bleachers to be seated. My pounding heart matched the high volumes of noise made by the students' voices, laughter, and movements. My mind's silent, overwhelming thoughts of "I can't do this" screamed louder than everything. I shook my head, trying to rid myself of my never-ending cycle of overthinking. My eyes flickered to the family section, where my parents sat in the second row of folding chairs. They made eye contact with me and grinned. I smiled back, even though I still felt uneasy about the situation.

Deciding to distract myself, I looked down at the sheet of paper with my poems, rehearsing again. After a few minutes, I glanced up to see a tall, middle-aged man with black-gray hair and deep brown eyes walk up to the podium. "Good morning, everyone," he said, leaning into the microphone. All the students, faculty, and parents quickly went from a soft chatter to silence. The man introduced himself as Paul Roberts, and I watched as he warmly welcomed his audience. He invited the girl sitting next to me to the podium. She stood and walked forward, taking her place in front of the microphone. Standing up straight, she began speaking, delivering a speech from the debate team. Her voice was confident and not the slightest bit shaky. I was unable to relate as my right foot tapped against the gym floor, and my trembling hands gripped the hem of my pleated skirt. I wanted to pay attention, but anticipation for what was about to occur left me lost in my thoughts.

When she finished, the audience applauded, and the girl left the podium, plopping herself back down in her seat. She gave me a warm, relaxed smile. I tried to return it, but I could tell I wasn't masking my anxiety well, as my grin felt forced and uneasy in contrast. Mr. Roberts walked to the podium and leaned toward the microphone once more. As my poems projected on the screen behind him, Mr. Roberts introduced me and invited me forward.

I swallowed hard. It was time.

I stood up and walked by Mr. Roberts, leading myself to the podium. My body felt numb and heavy, and my legs felt like Jello. I took another large breath. Placing the sheet of paper with my poems on the smooth, wooden platform, I leaned toward the microphone. My lips parted, a little shaky at first, and I began speaking, starting with my first poem, "Wrath." As I spoke, I looked to my audience. The crowd was silent, one thousand pairs of eyes staring at me. Bright lights blurred my view as I looked forward. I had a flashback to when I used to dance at the age of seven. Back then, I was too young to let my anxiety get in my head, so I didn't mind dancing in front of a crowd of people. I was performing again, except this time, I was much more nervous. My hands, slippery with sweat, gripped the edges of the podium as my legs trembled from behind the stand.

But then something strange happened. As I began my second poem, "Love," I realized that the more I spoke, the more self-confident I became. The words rolled off of my tongue, like they were more than ready to present themselves to the world. Here I was, standing in front of a thousand people, and for once, I felt powerful, as if nothing could shake me. When I finished, the applause was louder than my heavy breathing, my racing heart, and my anxious thoughts. I heard some students from my class cheer my name as I stared out at the sea of people. As I made my way back to my seat, I smiled—a wide smile that displayed both rows of my teeth.

Relief washed over me; it was all over. Weeks ago, the idea of speaking in front of a large audience terrified me; yet, here I was, discovering a new confidence within me that I didn't know I had as I heard the cheers and the applause around me. My heart swelled with warmth and excitement. It was suddenly made clear to me that I should be more confident in myself and in my writing, for I overcame my fear in this moment and excelled more than I ever thought I could. With my poem, "Love," ending on a positive note and seeing the smiles in the audience, I also realized that I wanted to keep exploring and writing poetry; I wanted my words to uplift, to inspire, and to make others smile. It was then that I wondered if poetry helped to define my overall writing goals.

When the assembly ended, a group of my friends sprinted forward to hug me tightly and praise me for my performance. Even people whom I hadn't talked to much approached with "congratulations" and "great job." As I made my way out of the gymnasium, a girl in the distance pointed at me and said to her friend, "Hey, that's the poetry girl." Poetry girl. I chuckled to myself.

It was then that I realized I wasn't just a fiction writer; I was also a poet. And later, I would be a children's book author, a nonfiction writer, and a screenwriter as well. Looking back to that day, I realize that this was a turning point in my life. I was vulnerable and courageous, placing my words out there for the world to read for the first time. I wrote poetry, a genre in which I had not yet explored all that much. Then, I read my poems in front of a thousand people when I had a fear of public speaking. And later, during my senior year of high school, I would take on a leadership role as editor-in-chief of the same literary magazine. I would help other authors get published and tell their stories. I would go on to study English and Creative Writing in college, further developing my craft and using my voice in the way I knew best. Even now, I can't say that I won't have any fear in the future, but at least I'm making progress. And progress is what matters most.

AARON SANDBERG

The Poetry Lesson

POETRY

AARON SANDBERG grew up outside of Chicago and has been teaching English full-time ever since graduating from Elmhurst College. Always sensitive to the written word, he's written creatively in some form for most of his life—including lyrics for his old band. However, his focus on poetry began in earnest around 2015. Receiving awards for his photography and teaching, poetry was always a peripheral interest until then. In 2020, with what started as a quarantine project to see more of his work in print, he published nearly one hundred pieces within a year—as well as earning a nomination for a Pushcart Prize. In an interview with *Asimov's Science Fiction* magazine, he spoke about the themes he finds himself turning toward: "I think I write a lot about the domestic, minutia, intimacy, loss, the past . . . I like putting objects in unfamiliar locations and seeing what happens." Aaron's work can be found in *West Trade Review*, *Sporklet*, *Lowestoft Chronicle*, *Abridged*, *Giallo*, *Right Hand Pointing*, *Monday Night*, and elsewhere.

It tells us to touch
the stove again.

So, please—
no lectures this time.

We've taken the moral
out of its mouth.

Still, hard to know
at worst and at best:

       all poems embarrass
       or burn us alive.

MARGARITA BARESSI

A Youthful Regret

NON-FICTION

A proud Boricua, MARGARITA BARESSI (b. 1961) was raised by her grandparents in San Juan, Puerto Rico. A desire to experience snow landed her at Boston University, where she majored in Public Relations. She subsequently enjoyed a 25-year career in journalism and marketing communications writing for PC Week (now eWeek) and working for such brands as Avon, Frito-Lay, and Dunkin Donuts. She later transitioned into writing creative non-fiction, focusing on crafting memoir and parenting essays, which have found homes in *Acentos Review*, *Your Teen Magazine*, *Grown and Flown*, *The Drowning Gull*, and others.

Her first novel, *A Delicate Marriage*, is set in 1930s and 40s Puerto Rico and is loosely based on the story of her grandparents. The manuscript was born during the competitive Novel Generator program at Boston's Grub Street, and led to a writer's residency at the prestigious Noepe Center for Literary Arts on Martha's Vineyard. It was also recognized as a finalist for the 2020 Pipeline unpublished manuscript award, in the literary fiction category.

Margarita's Puerto Rican roots and values fully inform every piece of who she is and every role she plays in life—woman, mother, wife, writer, friend, mentor, relative. She considers herself Puerto Rican first, everything else second. Every day, in some way, she's reminded of how little Americans know about this U.S. territory, and makes it her mission to educate others about her island home. Such was the impetus for her first and soon-to-be subsequent novels.

I pushed open the heavy glass doors and inhaled the slightly stale air that, to me, tasted exotic, exhilarating, and absolutely right. I'd transferred from Boston University's Business School to the College of Communication and was impatient to get started. Gleefully, I entered the Journalism 101 classroom and took in the dusty chalkboard smell, the rows of typewriters atop worn wooden tables disguised as desks, and Professor Drake*, he of the craggy face and silver leonine mane. I was going to learn so much from him.

I sat with confidence, surrounded by my people (I'd finally found them!) and waited for my future to begin. Prof. Drake outlined the basics of journalistic writing, the who/what/where/when/why, and the inverted pyramid method of recounting information. But I barely heard him. I was exceedingly preoccupied with the machine in front of me. Dull black, compactly square, and keys emerging from its body like claws, this typewriter was not just old, it was a bonafide antique. What the hell *was* this? I glanced around the room. All the typewriters were, if not identical, similar versions of the one facing me. None of the other students seemed the least bit concerned, but maybe they didn't know any better. I was a seasoned sophomore fulfilling a freshman requirement, and I recognized these machines were Trouble.

After Prof. Drake informed us we'd be completing in-class assignments every time we met, I whispered to a fellow student, "What's with these typewriters? I mean, they're ancient."

"Yeah," he responded with a shrug. "They don't have enough electric ones for all the classrooms, so freshmen get these." *Great.*

When the class met next, I tried to select the least battle-weary machine and settled in, ready to work. Prof. Drake handed out reprints of old Associated Press (AP) news feeds: stories reported by AP writers and distributed to newsrooms across the country. At his command, we were to crank out the lead paragraph of our own news story based on this already professionally written AP copy. Oh, and we had a limited amount of time to complete our task. Very limited. With shaking hands, I fed a sheet of paper into the typewriter's roller and turned the knob to secure the paper in place. I scanned the AP copy, wasted precious seconds wracking my brain to find a different way of saying the same thing, and started to type. Well, I *attempted* to type.

Maybe I could have made those keys move with a semblance of swiftness, had my fingers been rubber mallets thrown down with the brute force of Hercules. Instead, I pounded on the letters with my thumbs and index fingers, my strongest digits, imploring the keys to reach the paper and make an imprint through the faded typewriter ribbon. Time propelled forward at hyperspeed until the last seconds were spent and I'd barely completed one sentence.

I surveyed the room. Most of the other students looked as stunned and overwhelmed as I felt.

"Who would like to volunteer for me to read their copy?" asked Prof. Drake.

What copy? You mean the half-sentence I composed?

A tall male student in the front row raised his hand, and Prof. Drake rattled off his perfectly written paragraph.

Are you kidding me? How the hell did that guy actually create a coherent paragraph? Does he have a secret electric typewriter up there?

My humiliation and disgust were all-encompassing. Would the challenge of having to rewrite perfectly good AP copy on a mastodon of a typewriter prove too arduous for me? The torment continued for several weeks, and while my ability to pound the keys improved slightly, I was getting unheard of Cs and Ds on these in-class assignments.

Then Prof. Drake assigned our first take-home piece, an art review. I was excited to hand in my review of *Oklahoma!*. I'd just seen the musical for the first time at the Metropolitan Center and noted how the theater's ancient heating system clanged along merrily to several of the songs. I knew the review was clever and well written, and I was thrilled to get it back, marked with a big red "A." Until I read the fine print: "I expect ALL of your future work to be of this caliber."

My body temperature spiked, nausea struck, sweat trickled down my torso, and I began to shake with indignation as I realized Prof. Drake thought *someone else* had written my piece.

No way.

I was proud of my work and knew I was a skilled writer. I'd be damned if I'd let this man, or anyone else, rob me of what was rightfully mine. Consumed with the need to clear my name and armed with anger-fueled courage, I burst into Prof. Drake's office. Trying to ignore the collection of oversized and intimidating African tribal masks that lined this white man's walls, I pleaded my case. I said I was no good at rewriting AP news feeds on old typewriters, that I needed to mull over a story before I wrote it, that I was a features writer, not a news reporter. He remained unmoved and gazed through me with tired eyes. He was an experienced professor who had seen "this kind of thing" before.

Throughout the semester, I continued to fail at in-class work and excel at the longer take-home assignments. Prof. Drake must have thought I had unlimited funds to pay my ghostwriters because I'm certain he never believed the writing was mine. Yet, I went on to ace my remaining writing-focused classes, none of which required banging out copy on-the-spot using instruments of torture. I had time to think, to plot and concoct, and the results spoke for themselves. Two professors even asked for copies of my assignments to use as examples with future students. At graduation, as I crossed the stage to receive my diploma, I wondered whether Prof. Drake heard the words "magna cum laude" after my name.

My student writing samples were strong enough to land me a job as an editorial assistant at a nascent magazine called *PC Week*, where I earned a promotion to features writer in less than a year. Oh, the luxury of writing on a personal computer! The sweet responsiveness of the keys, the ease of making corrections, the pleasure of thinking through a story—I'd come a long way from Journalism 101. At twenty-two, I was interviewing heads of IT at major corporations and showcasing best practices for implementing personal computers in the workplace in feature-length stories.

I fantasized about sending Prof. Drake a collection of tear sheets of my articles, my beautiful byline front and center, maybe even highlighted in yellow.

But I never did.

*The professor's name has been changed to protect the oppressor's identity.

DERYCK N. ROBERTSON

Long List

POETRY

DERYCK N. ROBERTSON (b. 1969) grew up in Toronto, Ontario, as the oldest of five children. He spent his summers messing around in the woods of Jackson's Point and Algonquin Park, which is where he lived out his love of the outdoors. Eventually, he took his canoe to Peterborough to attend Sir Sandford Fleming College and Trent University before receiving his B.Ed. from the University of Windsor. Robertson currently teaches Grade 7 and is active in his community through Scouting and The Salvation Army.

His work is observational and is influenced by nature, the outdoors, and his family. His writing has recently found a larger audience as he has begun to send work out into the world instead of hoarding it in Moleskine notebooks and on Tim Horton's napkins. Humor infuses much of his work because, "life is hard enough, and we all need to laugh more." Robertson's two self-published zines, *January* and *Ten*, have found a small, yet receptive, readership. His literary magazine passion has since extended to the writing community with *Canoe Lake Memories*, celebrating the life and creative work of adventurer and artist Tom Thomson via Robertson's very own Paddler Press, mid 2021.

His mom is particularly proud of his accomplishments. He hasn't won any awards for his writing yet, but is willing to make an exception if the money is right.

So, the long list is out today
for the CBC's 2016 Poetry Prize:
twenty-nine names.
I'm sure my name is there,
but they obviously spelled it wrong.
Called me Susan,
or Richard, or Karl.
An oversight, I'm sure.
And my words are all there,
just in the wrong order.
Darn auto-correckt.
What? No misteak?
My bad.
Guess that's why I wasn't asked to submit a digital self-portrait.
The apologetic email says that I may even submit
the same poem next year.
The apologetic email says that I may even submit
the same poem next year.
The apologetic email says that I may...
Maybe if I make up some new words,
words that sound deep, like hobbinating (verb /Hä-bi-nā-tiŋ/)
Or move the lines around the page.
                            like this
or this
                                    and, write, it, in, little
                    paragraph, stanzas, even

        with, lots, of, commas, like, Atwood
        (Can-con reference for
        added emphasis and impact.
        Judges *LOVE* Atwood.) And I LOVE George,

Erin, and Roo. Probably should have
mentioned that earlier . . .

I only have one question:
Is the twenty-five bucks tax-deductible?

JENN JARRETT

Choosing Success

CREATIVE NON-FICTION

JENN JARRETT was raised in Alabama by an aeronautics engineer and an algebra teacher who encouraged her young interest in science. After discovering the magical world of fiction, her education turned to English, studying the manipulation of words and the beauty in storytelling.

She's published several science and technology articles under various pseudonyms since 2006, including many in the *Whyville Times* as a teen. Jenn's writing, no matter the genre, involves a heavy layer of introspection, and she hopes to instill a sense of individuality and personal reflection in her readers.

What if? The idea blooms like watercolors across the page. This could be it. This could be the perfect debut.

A pen scratches letters through a pastel notebook saved for such a story. A single thought stretches, and half the pages fill. But something is missing. The excitement and joy fades like the steam from a half-sipped hot chocolate. This isn't it. The notebook slides back on its shelf, but another slips off to take its place on folded legs.

What if? Scents of juniper and apples waft from their flickering candles and soak into the story of crispy leaves and swampy settings. A protagonist commits crimes, a misunderstood creature falls in love, and an enemy becomes an ally. This is better. This could be it. But even with an outline, the plot falls apart. The villain wins, and the notebook slides back on its shelf.

"What's your story about?"

I don't know.

"When will you be published?"

I don't know.

"Why do you write?"

I don't know.

What if? The thought drifts back. Keys click, their sharp edges scraping fingertips. Rejection stabs into the pages and becomes a tragedy thrashed by darkness and mayhem. This could be it. This could be the chosen one. But what if it's not?

The words flow like rapids beyond the pool of rocky doubts, and its purpose becomes clear. It doesn't have to be the one, the best, or a classic. Chosen success doesn't rely on publication. It emerges from discovery—from the journey.

"What's your story about?"

My passions.

"When will you be published?"

Doesn't matter.

"Why do you write?"

To grow.

DANIEL HINDS

Author Bio

PROSE POETRY

DANIEL HINDS lives in Newcastle, UK, where he also grew up. His mother sought to pass on her enjoyment of literature by reading the Harry Potter books aloud to him at bedtime. Clearly, no such encouragement was needed, as this was usually undertaken while he silently read a concealed copy of the next book in the series. He further developed an interest in literature, during his time studying English Literature at Newcastle University. He went on to win two prestigious scholarships, the School Bursary Award and Excellence Scholarship, for his English Literature 1500-1900 MA, graduating with a Distinction and top of his course. It was while reading Ted Hughes's *Tales from Ovid* at university that he first realized he wanted to be a poet.

He won the Poetry Society's Timothy Corsellis Young Critics Prize 2018 and his experimental prose poem review of Jay Bernard's *Surge* was one of the winners of the Shortlist Book Review Competition 2020, held in celebration of the Dylan Thomas Prize by Swansea University. Daniel's poetry is known for being mythic, allusive, inter-textual, and witty.

Daniel started submitting his poetry concentratedly near the end of 2019 and has since been published in literary magazines, anthologies, and newspaper. He has additionally explanded his skill for an audio piece, based on his poetic sequence *The Stone Men of Newcastle*, about the statues of the city, which was commissioned by New Creatives, a talent development scheme supported by Arts Council England and BBC Arts, and delivered by Tyneside Cinema.

HE has been rejected by various prestigious publications, a girl whom he loved for her silver braces when his hair was still white with youth, St. Peter at the pearly white gates, several creditors, and when he split up with his girlfriend, by the dog when they made him choose. His publications have caused a lasting impact (on the environment). At university, he was awarded a prestigious sum of student debt (which he will never pay back), white guilt (which he will never make reparations for), a sense of entitlement (a liking for long poem titles, and even longer lists of letters after his name), and skills in critical analysis (just enough to know he will never be rich). As well as further skills, like sleeping in, and learning to cohabit with the intolerable. He has been the writer-in-residence for the basement of his mother's house. He has won several impressive fellowships, consisting of the standard and extended editions of Jackson's first Tolkien film, at the office tombola. Below is a link to his website, which invariably fails to load, like a spider's web used as a pallet for a 10 ton truck. You can follow him on social media, but he won't follow you back. He dislikes endings of gentle humor, usually about coffee or deliberate hobbies, and a weird fun fact. He can time travel, as shown by his ten years out-of-date author headshot.

DEE RICHARDS

Meine Geschichte

FICTION

DEE RICHARDS (b. 1982) is a 3rd generation San Diegan and the first of her working poor family to attend a major university since her father left to fight in the Vietnam War. Options for a poor, bisexual, gender-fluid goth kid are simple: clean up your act and get a job or straighten up and get married. Dee found herself married at nineteen to an abuser and spent the next six years in hell. Finally clawing their way out of the darkness, Dee emerged victorious—but not without the scars which formed them. Twenty years after writing a story about a dog who wished it were a cat on an old typewriter her mom gave her for her eighth birthday, Dee dared to dream of a life free from the prison of "can't."

Dee won a national essay award, a sci-fi writing award, and still didn't know if they had what it took. Dee earned praise from professors—"wow, amazing," "you are a beautiful, gifted writer"—and still wasn't quite sure. Dee has since been accepted to one of the top ten public universities in the USA to pursue their writing dream and is finally starting to believe that she might actually be onto something. Dee has been published with *Epoch Press*, *The Cabinet of Heed Literary Magazine*, *Daily Drunk Magazine*, and featured in her community college's "New Voices" event to showcase rising talent. Now, she/they will rise far beyond the limitations of what was. Dee thrives in Irvine, CA with their partner and two children.

She gave birth in her sleep. It was impossible, especially considering that she lacked interest in partnering traditions that would lead to such an occurrence. But cries woke her nonetheless—small, mewling screams of a hungry child. The tiny body wriggled helplessly between her legs, in a pool of blood and mucus. There was no doubt that this child was born of her, so she simply drew it near to her breast. It suckled painfully, but she did not pull away, for she already loved the tiny child.

After the baby calmed, she wrapped her in a blanket, resting her tiny head upon her bare chest. She anticipated weariness but was instead bursting with excitement. Although she had never wanted a child, she was now filled with joy at the thought of her dream made flesh. Her mind raced with hopes for her daughter: places she would go, languages she would learn, lives she would touch.

Their eyes locked, and peace spread within her. She had created something flawless, as beautiful as the morning sun. This child would change the world, she knew that without a doubt. Her finger delicately curled the baby's red hair and petted her soft cheek. Calmness enveloped their embrace, and they drifted off to sleep together.

They awoke entwined in the baby's swaddling cloth, inseparable. Though they'd only rested a few hours, her little one was now a toddler. She puzzled at the babe's curly hair springing from her head, her body now heavy in her mother's arms.

"Mommy!" said her child.

"Yes, my dear! What shall I call you?"

"Li-Ma!" the babe squealed.

"Lima is beautiful," said the mother, gently kissing her child's forehead. "Let's take you into the world, my dear Lima!"

They bathed in warm water, keeping each other close. The woman could not remember her name any longer, only that she was now "Mommy," which suited her.

Mommy took her miracle to meet new friends. Some swooned, speaking in adoring tones of her ability to produce something so lovely and magical, while others criticized her tale of how Lima came to be. By the end of the day, Lima walked entirely on her own and was already outgrowing the small dress that Mommy had bought.

Mommy loaded a shopping cart with clothes in every size, trying to accommodate Lima's changes. People at every stop shot off suggestions: "Keep her in smaller sizes, then she won't grow so fast!" "Don't feed her so much, you want to keep her small!" and "Baggier clothes are better to grow into." Mommy just showered her little creation with anything her heart desired.

By bedtime, Mommy's creaky twin mattress was getting a little cramped for two. Lima's arms and legs drooped off the sides as she slept, and Mommy didn't rest much, trying to keep Lima from falling. By morning, Mommy knew that she and Lima needed space to grow, and that was when Madame Editrice knocked.

"I would love to take Lima to my home; there are countless young women who, under my careful tutelage, emerge perfected!" Madame Editrice proposed. Lima sat quietly on their shared bed, pretending she didn't know what was happening.

"Well, I really don't know how to care for her—I wasn't expecting to be a mother." Mommy admitted.

"We have a program for you as well, to learn how to care for a child of her unique gifts." Madame Editrice placed a gloved hand on her shoulder.

"Can I bring her home once I've completed the program?" Mommy asked, staring lovingly at Lima, afraid to lose the most beautiful thing she had ever beheld.

"Of course, dear! She will be excellent by then, and you will be ready for her!" Madam Editrice laughed, her voice high and sharp.

"If it's what's best for Lima," Mommy said. Madame Editrice collected Lima, eyes sad but eager for the world before her.

Mommy attended the training program suggested by Madam Editrice. The classes were long and seemed only to reinforce her instincts, but she occasionally found a gem of information. Through every test and reading, she pictured Lima and the perfect life they could have together.

During this time, Lima had grown so much that when

Mommy visited, she barely recognized the babe she had once held in her arms.

"She has a wonderful voice!" Madame Editrice exclaimed.

"Does she?" Mommy felt ashamed that she didn't know.

"C'est magnifique!"

"I can see how much she's grown. Is she ready to come home yet?" Mommy worried. Madam Editrice's shrill laugh was silenced by Lima walking between them.

"I am performing tonight, Mommy!" Lima's voice rang through the air.

"I am so proud of you!" Mommy was happy, but she felt a deep pang of longing wrap across her back and into her arms and fingers. As Lima performed, Mommy felt she barely knew that which had once been a part of her, as familiar as her own fingerprints. Mommy wept but hid her tears. The audience's applause was an uproar, shaking Mommy from her sorrow, allowing Lima her fame.

As time wore on, Lima visited less, but Mommy's days were filled with new "friends" and old enemies suddenly warming. Mommy grew weary from the weeks without Lima, the blank expressions of adoration at her ability to produce such a miracle reflected nothing of her pain at the loss of her dear one. Loneliness locked her into the home they had once shared. Mommy watched videos of Lima's successes and read clipped newspaper articles. A few of them even mentioned Mommy, but more as an aside to Lima's meteoric rise. Mommy's heart had become a swamp of putrefying emptiness when she thought it might be time to have another child. She wanted to hold something brand new in her hands again, something uniquely hers. But, just as Mommy sat at her mahogany desk, fingers poised, Lima burst into the small apartment.

"Mommy?!" Lima's red hair gleamed, and her eyes shone like starlight.

"Yes, my darling one?" Mommy was overjoyed but hesitant to hold the child who was now so different.

"They want to make a movie about ME!" she squealed.

"Oh?" Mommy hugged her, gently pressing in desperation to fuse Lima back to her own body, but Lima pulled away.

"Yes! They said there need to be a few changes—is that okay? No one will ever believe that you gave birth overnight, that I grew so fast. They are going to give us both A LOT of money for it!" Lima bounced.

Mommy froze for a moment, absorbing the weight of the news—Lima was no longer the babe she'd wrapped her whole world in, but a product of her own. A limb had been torn from Mommy, and here it stood, angered at the body it had once shared.

"You are mine, Lima," Mommy said in a paced tone.

Lima spun toward Mommy with a threatening glare.

"After everything Madame Editrice did for us?!"

"You were supposed to come back," Mommy cried in a panic.

Lima slammed her hand on the wall. "You gave me to her, what did you expect?" she screamed.

"I was trying to do what was best for you."

"No, you were trying to do what was best for *you*!" Lima snapped.

"But Lima, you were *my* story, never your own," Mommy pleaded.

"And now, you must let me go." Papers scattered around the room as Lima slammed the door; one piece of Mommy's soul, forever gone.

ANISHA KAUL

On Not Writing

POETRY

ANISHA KAUL (b. 1996) grew up at various places before the family settled in New Delhi. She was unaware that these simple movements were to shape the essence of her identity. Her roots trace back to Kashmir, which her parents and her community were forced to leave in 1990 under the most unfortunate circumstances. She said, "I inherited their exile at my birth and my existence is that of a genocide survivor. Questions of belonging have been a great discomfort to me." With each passing day, she breathes shared memories and her lost ancestral home. Later, as she earned her bachelor's and master's degree in English literature, her literary output proved to be cathartic. Kaul served in the capacity of the editor for her college magazine *Pramila*, 2016-17 issue.

Kaul began her writing career by publishing poetry in her undergrad college magazine and has since found beautiful homes for thirty-five of them in various reputed national and international print and online anthologies including *The Indian Feminist Review*, *Ethel Zine*, *Splintered Disorder Press*, *Fevers of the Mind*, *From the Farther Tree*, and *Analogies & Allegories Literary Magazine*, among others. She most often pens free verses with abstract themes, alternate realities, or a longing for home. Kaul dreams to author a memoir in remembrance of all that she has lost.

Words slumber in some forgotten corner
As each day spreads a fresh layer of dust over
My mind and the scattered pages
A few words scribbled on the edges
Stare blankly at the opposite wall
While, at my touch, the reluctant pen stumbles
From grace into a darker alley
There, it befriends the long lost inspiration
Together, they conspire against me

Restless, I open the shutters

The busy days have silently melted away
With the moonless sky pinned to the horizon
My gentle muse has gone unseen for long
Now, resting on the frame, I await her return

VALERIE HUNTER

Elegy For The Poems I Almost Wrote

POETRY

VALERIE HUNTER has always been a voracious reader with a love of stories and started writing her first novel in the third grade. She began submitting stories and poems for publication while majoring in English/ Secondary Education at the College of New Jersey and went on to earn an MFA in Writing for Children and Young Adults from Vermont College of Fine Arts. She teaches high school English and continues to write in a wide variety of genres.

Hunter's stories and poems have appeared in numerous magazines and journals, including *Cricket*, *Cicada*, *Hopscotch*, *Edison Literary Review*, *Room*, *Other Voices*, *Wizards in Space*, *Paper Lanterns*, *Colp*, and *Storyteller*, as well as anthologies such as *Brave New Girls*, *When the World Stopped*, *(Re)Sisters*, and *One Thousand Words for War*. When writing, she tries to follow the same advice she gives her students: "Focus on a small moment and try to bring it to life. Make every word count."

They existed briefly—
fragments of thoughts,
flashes of inspiration,
those perfect lines flitting through
at inopportune moments:
while driving or teaching,
in the shower, or drifting off to sleep;
lines unable to be captured
in anything as permanent as ink.
I tried to hold onto them,
repeating them over and over
to myself, convinced they'd stick,
that I'd be able to recall them later
at a more convenient time,
that they belonged to me
in solid form instead
of being the ghosts
that they were, drifting away,
disintegrating, disappearing.

I'd like to say I've learned my lesson,
that I've stashed tiny notebooks everywhere
in order to be better prepared,
that I'm more willing to crawl
out of bed or pull to the side of the road
in the name of inspiration, to capture
those fleeting lines. And perhaps I am
a little better, scribbling fragments
on scraps and in margins,
trying to preserve them until
I can turn them into something more.

But they're never as good
as the poems I lost,
which I'm certain were brilliant
because there's no evidence
to contradict it, nothing
to prove me wrong.

MICHELLE TANG

Message In A Novel

FICTION

MICHELLE TANG was born in Manila, Philippines, and immigrated to Canada at a young age. She has always been a voracious reader, and the books from her local library developed both her English and a passion for speculative fiction. In 2017, Michelle began to write seriously and published the first story she submitted, "Contract Killer," in an anthology published by the Canadian Author Association and Iguana Books. Since then, her work has been featured in a dozen other anthologies, including *Terrifying Ghosts*, *Night Terrors, Vol. II*, and *Once Upon an Enchanted Forest*. She often incorporates characters and elements of her Asian culture into her pieces, something she felt was missing in the books she grew up reading. Given her career as an oncology nurse, many of Michelle's stories focus on the brevity of life and its accompanying emotions. Her reviewed work has been praised as "absolutely [nailing] that tone of sad wistfulness" (For Aeternum) and "a lovely meditation on love and loss" (Banshee Song).

The used bookstore was no different than the dozens he'd visited in the past. The shelves were shoulder-height in the center of the room and stretched to the ceiling along the walls. The scent of aged paper and dust greeted him a moment before the cashier did, her eyes lighting up with recognition.

"I can't believe it," she squealed. She looked around the store for any other potential fans, but no one looked their way. "Danielle" was written in bubbly letters on her name tag.

Jason's cheeks burned, but he forced the words out anyway. "Do you have any used copies of *Until I Leave You?*" God, why was he still doing this? After three years of fruitless searching, hadn't he put himself through enough?

Danielle grinned. "It was your first best-seller, wasn't it? I thought you'd have a copy."

"Me too." He tried to keep his voice light, but the pain always seemed to leak through. He forced a smile. "Is that a yes, then?"

"Right this way."

Danielle led him through the maze of shelves stacked high with used books. She turned to gaze at him so often she could have been doing pirouettes. Under her scrutiny, Jason's cane suddenly seemed over-large, obvious, and geriatric. He imagined the way he must look, pallid skin hanging off sharp cheekbones and bunching beneath his eyes like ill-fitting clothing.

"You're one of my favorite writers," Danielle said. "I've read everything you've ever written, probably a dozen times."

"That's so kind of you to say." How large was this bookstore?

She stopped by a shelf identical to the others. "Right here, Mr. Cho." She tapped at the creased spine. "Do you want me to ring it up for you?"

"I'm searching for a specific copy. I just need a moment to look through it, please."

"Sure thing. I'll come check on you in a few." Danielle danced away.

Jason's hand trembled as he pulled the book from the shelf. It was the right cover, the first one ever printed. He flipped to the title page and saw his autograph, bold and faded with age. *Help me, Charlotte. Let this be the sign I've been waiting for.*

Forty years ago, when his first novel had come out, he'd gone into every bookstore he passed and autographed each copy. He'd been returning the book to its shelf when a woman approached him.

"Oh, is that the last one?" Her lips made a disappointed moue.

"It's okay. You can have it."

"I couldn't take it from you. You were here first."

She was gorgeous, this stranger, and Jason was suddenly sure she wouldn't believe him if he said he'd written it, or worse, she would believe him but think him such an arrogant braggart that she'd walk away. All he could manage was a weak, "No, please. I don't want it."

The woman had appraised Jason for a moment, her head tilted before she nodded, as if to herself. "How about this, then? You read it first, and then when you're finished, you give me a call. My name's Charlotte." She took the pen from Jason's shirt pocket and flipped to the very back. She scrawled a message and was returning both pen and book to him when she stopped to look at the author's picture on the back cover.

Charlotte had been the first to look at him with eyes full of wonder. It was a look he would never have imagined could be directed at him, not from a cool and confident woman like her. Jason's heart fluttered like book pages in a breeze.

"In that case," she'd said, grabbing the book to her chest, "I *will* take it."

She later gave him her number outside the store, scribbled on the back of the receipt, and winked a goodbye. He'd gripped the waxy paper between careful fingers, and as she walked away, felt his heart skip in time with her fading footsteps.

•

Jason flipped to page thirteen. There was a small blue drop in the middle of the yellowed page, and hope pushed like a tiny seedling through the brambles of his grief. *Don't get carried away, old man. You've been wrong before.*

139

On their third date, Charlotte had been drinking a blue raspberry slushie with his book open on her lap. They sat in his old Honda Accord in the parking lot of a convenience store, the light from the neon signs on the store window coloring their faces pink. He'd cleaned his car before their date, and the pine-scented air freshener hanging from the rearview mirror clashed with the artificial berry smell of Charlotte's slushie. The late August breeze blew in through their open windows, warm and moist against their skin, like an exhaled breath. They'd had some plan to go to the movies but talked so long they missed all the showtimes. He never thought he would find someone as excited about his book as he was, but she wanted to know everything, and he was happy to talk as long as it kept her beside him.

"Jason, something about this book really speaks to me. I've never read anything like it."

Utter joy had filled him—a moment where he felt exposed and seen and accepted—but doubt followed close behind. It was as if a sunbeam illuminated him, a sign from the heavens that he was doing what he had been born to do, before a storm cloud crept in to cut off the golden warmth.

"You're just saying that to get in my pants." He'd leaned over to take a sip of her slushie, the cold tart sweetness as exhilarating to his taste buds as the woman was to his soul. A drop spilled from the top of the straw to land on a page, blue interweaving with grey-white fibres, impossible to separate, and thereafter forever changed . . .

•

Jason closed the used book and shut his eyes. He breathed in the musty scent of aging paper and tried to control his shaking knees. For a moment, he considered asking Danielle for a chair, but the idea was quickly quashed. If he'd finally found Charlotte's copy, he wanted—no, he needed—this privacy.

When his heart rate had slowed, he began to flip through the book again. Page thirty-seven had a round patch where the letters were faded.

•

She'd been so surprised. Her dark eyebrows had lifted,

and her brown eyes widened, but the most obvious sign of her shock was that her mouth had dropped open. The pink chewing gum she'd been blowing into a bubble had fallen out onto the ever-present book, popping as it hit the page.

Charlotte swore and began to pick at the gum carefully. Whole typed words were visible on the pink mess she peeled off, the way Jason used silly putty to lift off the printed text in his school books.

"Is that a yes?" Jason asked from their kitchen floor, where he waited on his knees. He wondered for a moment if she hated the ring, bought with his third royalty check. *Until I Leave You* was still an international bestseller, and he was starting to get recognized by book-lovers, but none of that would mean anything unless Charlotte was by his side.

She leaned down to kiss him, a long, sweet kiss which gave him his answer. "Of course, it's a yes, my love. It's always been a yes. Now, help me get this gum off."

•

Jason began to flip through the pages faster, suddenly afraid his mind was playing tricks on him because he wanted this to be Charlotte's book so badly. It felt like the last chance he would ever have to hear from her. The quiet sounds of the store and customers passing by faded into the distance. The book in his hands was the only thing real to him.

The imperfections on the pages triggered memories, like a slideshow in his mind. But every used book bore marks and stains from its previous owners. He needed something unique, indisputable. Here. Page two-hundred and thirteen. A brown handprint, the creases and fingers impossibly small but perfectly formed. This was real.

•

"Emma's gotten into the pudding, I see." Charlotte gave him a kiss as she took off her coat, still in scrubs. "And she's learned to read my favorite book—how advanced for an eighteen-month-old."

"It's impossible to write with her and Noah here all day. I get nothing done. They don't even nap at the same time." Jason tried to sound calm, but deadlines loomed, and the constant pressure dried and blew away all his words—tumbleweeds in the barren desert of his once-creative mind.

"They'll be old soon enough, and you'll miss when they were this small."

"Why do you even leave the book out all the time, anyway? It's not like you read it anymore," he said.

"I do so." She washed her hands. "Every day, I read a few lines. It starts my day off with a bit of beauty."

"You could try to read something new for a change. You might get some new ideas in your head for once." It was unfair and untrue. His wife devoured books, but she always went back to this one. He wanted to take the words back, but frustration choked him, and he glared at her instead.

She squinted at him, and he forced himself not to look away first. "It's not my head that needs new ideas, is it, Jason? Why don't we ask my parents to watch the kids for a few days, give you some peace and quiet, okay?"

He nodded, suddenly ashamed. "I'm sorry, Charlotte. I don't deserve you."

She took the book away from the kitchen table, wiped at a handprint, saw it was dried, and sighed. "Of course you do, darling. We deserve each other."

•

There wasn't much more damage to the book. As Charlotte had predicted, their noisy, chaotic house had become quiet and peaceful too soon. They grew old, but they were happy, and the wonder never left Charlotte's eyes or Jason's heart. The kids visited on weekends and had even read Jason's books. But the intense, early years had left more of an impression on the parents and pages than the decades of calm that came after.

Jason stopped at page three-hundred and twelve and brushed trembling fingers against the moisture-damaged paper, the edges rough and uneven.

•

There hadn't been much time between her cancer diagnosis and her admission to the palliative care ward. Jason lived in her hospital room, finishing the ever-growing amounts of food she'd leave on the plates, jangling with too much coffee, and weeping while she slept. When Charlotte fell into a coma, Jason would read to her from his own book, hours a day, every day, until his voice was hoarse. He wanted to make sure her last days were full of the same beauty she'd reached for every morning of her life.

He was with her when her irregular breaths became long, slow gasps. He gripped her frail hand and whispered in her ear. "You can go, Charlotte. I love you, and I will be fine. The kids are here, and . . . we'll all be fine. Just . . . please send me a sign that you're okay. That we'll be together again."

When her body was still, Jason buried his face against her neck and wept. The book had lain forgotten by her shoulder, and when Jason cared enough to look for it, he found the pages soaked with tears. He'd been trying to absorb the moisture with a towel when a giant fist had clenched around his chest, like his heart was physically breaking. The scared, tear-streaked faces of his grown children loomed above him before all went black.

Jason awoke with an IV and a line of staples down his sternum. Emma sat curled in a chair by his bedside, and she gave him a small, exhausted smile.

"We took all of mom's stuff home, Dad. Don't you worry about a thing. Just focus on getting better. The doctor said you have to avoid stress."

When he was discharged, weeks later, he was taken to a half-empty house. He screamed as he stalked through the rooms, raging at the empty drawers, and demanded the objects which were strictly Charlotte's. He'd felt cheated—robbed of the therapeutic anguish in packing Charlotte's clothes away, sorting through her things, staring too long at photographs gone blurry with years and tears.

Noah shook his head, palms outward as though he wanted to push his father's anger away. "We donated it all, Dad. We thought it would give you another attack if you came home and had to deal with all of it. I'm sorry."

"The book—your mother's book! What did you do with it?"

"We . . . Emma gave all of Mom's books to a used book-store."

•

Emma had taken him to the store, but the book had already been sold. Jason became a ghost, haunting the same old places, checking week after week for Charlotte's copy. It became a bit of an obsession, and he knew the kids worried about him. After years—had it really been years?—of forcing smiles at awestruck store clerks, of hope dashed by disappointment, he'd given up.

He'd come to visit Noah's new house this afternoon to relay the doctor's prognosis. The bookstore had caught his eye on the drive home, and on a whim, he'd parked the car to try his luck one more time. The truth was, the chance of Jason finding Charlotte's book again after three years was so slim that only divine intervention would allow it to happen.

And now, Charlotte's sign was in his hands. He was sure of it. There was just one more thing to check. Jason turned to the last page of the book where, forty years ago, a young woman had scrawled a message.

The old man wept, right there in the bookstore, to see the familiar handwriting. Above her phone number, long discon-nected, Charlotte had written: *Call me when you reach the end. I'll be waiting.*

"Mr. Cho? Are you . . . oh my—are you all right?" Danielle had come back, her hand gripping her phone, and Jason realized she was ready to call for help.

"I'm more than fine, Danielle. I . . . I'm ready to go."

The young woman regained some of her cheer by the time they returned to the cash register. "It's a really wonderful book, Mr. Cho. It makes me cry every time I read it as well."

Jason smiled at her, the anger and grief inside him finally cooling. "And yet, the most important words inside this book are the ones I didn't write."

DALE PARNELL

The Poet's Truth

POETRY

DALE PARNELL was born in Norwich in the 1980's, and his love of books and reading started early. "There's a photograph of me aged three or four, completely engrossed in a heavy hardback book. The fact that I was holding the book upside down doesn't seem to have put me off at all." Dale attended university in Staffordshire, studying Film Production and making several attempts at finding work as a script writer. After university, Dale remained in Staffordshire, writing short film scripts and trying his hand at song writing before turning to short stories. He met his wife in the mid 2000's whilst they worked at the same office, and they married in 2014. "I don't know exactly what prompted me to start taking the short story writing seriously. But it does coincide nicely with meeting my wife, and so maybe part of me was trying to show off a little."

Dale self-published his first collection of short stories, *The Green Cathedral*, in 2017, leading to a second collection in 2019, *Bramble and Other Stories*. He received a commendation for his submission to the 2019 "There's No Planet B Stafford" Green Arts festival, and went on to win third place the following year. In 2020, Dale was nominated for the Pushcart Prize for his poem "In Silence," to be published by Paper Djinn Press. Dale's poetry has been described as moving, and at times humorous, and he continues to write both fiction and poetry. "I have found over the past couple of years that my favorite poetry comes from being honest about myself, my fears and occasionally my failings. I'm always in awe of poets who are willing to bare their souls, and often these are the most poignant."

What truth is there in poetry?
In phrases carved and molded
To fit the poet's plan?
A blustering cavalcade of re-imagined worlds,
Where poets profess their hearts.
Does opinion count for more when told in verse?
Should social change be so rehearsed and staged
In the back room of a pub or café?

The poet's voice will crack and strain,
And the good ship Righteous Indignation shall sail
On a sea of spittle flung
From the poet's pompous lungs.
Or perhaps a tear,
Forged by bittersweet heartache
That the poet stirs
From deep within.

Poetry is the fiction we wrap the world within.
It is the pinprick hole through which we see
The poet's cardboard stage,
Where the actors are but phantoms
And every word is delicately picked,
Discarded,
Renewed, replaced, replayed again and again,
Until the poet's truth is ready
To share with gathered friends.

We celebrate the art form.
We sit in murmured hush as each new voice
Stands in place of the old.

And we are told that *this time*,
This time our words will not be ignored.
Our anguished sighs and furious cries
Will find their way to the ears of the few.
Their hearts will be turned,
An alchemy of verse
That will ignite the world,
For our point of view shall be heard
And truth shall be acknowledged.

CORAL RIVERA

We Will Not Let You Go

CREATIVE NON-FICTION

Originally from Puerto Rico, CORAL RIVERA (b. 1986) was raised in Oviedo, Florida, just outside of Orlando. She grew up within the aura of Walt Disney World and so believed that magic was real—even if she had to be the one to create it. She just wasn't quite sure how until middle school when, amongst family struggles which led her to spend a long summer with her family in Puerto Rico, she found escapism in writing stories, and never looked back.

Coral has published one previous novel, entitled *A Deathly Compromise*, which has plans to be re-released in the near future. She is currently working on her second novel, a genre-bending fictional work entitled *Shift*.

Coral's work encapsulates her personal journeys and struggles, but in the lens of fanstical, sometimes mythological, protagonists. One of her signatures is to include the music which inspires the story somehow in the work itself—whether its in landmarks or chapter titles or full on scenes based on songs themselves —there will always be little Easter eggs to look for. It is her fondest hope for others to find solace and healing in reading her characters as much as she did in writing them. Her mission moving forward in her writing career is bring more Puerto Rican characters to the forefront of fictional fantasy tales.

The day broke open with the sound of "Bohemian Rhapsody."

I could tell from the scratch of the record player it was going to be one of those mornings. Again.

I pulled the covers over my head and groaned.

Thick footsteps tightened the sheets around me—fuck it all if she were bothered to take her boots off before getting into bed—and I ground my teeth until the all too familiar pain shot up my neck. I peeked over the top of the covers to glare at her. She had a pillow cradled in her arm and was air-guitaring to the solo, mouthing the words and paying no heed to the fact that it was eight in the morning, and I was in no mood to do anything other than lie there.

"Stop it."

She lifted the pillow into the air as the crescendo erupted, her hands gripping the cotton like a priceless instrument worthy of every note reverberating against the walls. Her eyes were closed, and she swayed to the guitar riff until the music wound down to the staccato. She punctuated each piano note by hitting me with the pillow until the opera found its way into the room.

Down feathers found their way up against my nose and lips and through my hair. "*Quit. It!*" I finally yelled, grabbing the pillow from her and throwing it onto the floor. I laid back down on my side and away from her, trying desperately to pull the sheets back over myself. She threw her body onto the bed and laid next to me. I could feel her eyes boring into the back of my head. Seconds seemed like minutes, and I couldn't stand the pinpointed predatory focus. I relented with a groan, turning to face her.

"*What?*"

She gave me a coy smile, and if she were anyone else, I'd want to erase it from existence. "Good morning, Sunshine."

"Dee, this needs to stop."

She crinkled her nose at me. Her eyeliner was impeccably winged, and I found myself envious and angry at the world all over again. She put a finger up to my nose and gently booped it. "Aww, you're cute, but no. Lots and lots to do today."

"You know I can't."

Dee sat up, her leather moto jacket raucously scrunching against her body. A pair of large headphones sat cradled around her neck, the string looping its way down to her hip. Her vintage relic of an mp3 player was off, but her headphones always remained on as if they were a part of her, an extra appendage of wire and rhythms. I had never known her without them. Freddie Mercury's vocals were starting to wind down, the outro of the rhapsody fading into the last set of vocals.

You're right, Freddie, I thought to myself. Nothing really did seem to matter. I closed my eyes, already bearing the guilt and weight of the feeling.

"There's a big difference between can't and won't, and you, baby girl, have a big case of *won't.*"

I sat up then and mirrored her pose. My eyes were still puffy from the night before, and the room was blurry without my contacts. She was clear, though. She was always clear as day. From across the room, I could see the stark white of my laptop with a blurred pink splotch of a floral "Latina" sticker in the bottom left-hand corner. I could feel my eyes already starting to well up.

It had been a week since the fallout.

My publisher, silent behind the curtain these past few weeks, had decided to burn the company down to its ashes. They were present when it was easy to flash their name in front of our stories, to push their tales at the front of the line and boast as if they were an Arthurian legend. They never expected it to be hard. They never expected to work for their titles. Instead, they lit the match in the form of a goodbye email not even two paragraphs long. My book, my story, my work—all gone. My free paperback copies were sitting in a box collecting dust, their pages still crisp and clinging to each other unperturbed. I once relished in the crackling of fresh pages being opened for the first time. Now, the sensation filled my heart with dread. Myself, my friends, my fellow storytellers, all left in the dust with the husk of a promise in their hands. Mine was given but ripped away, its scars leaving a burning sensation on my fingertips. It hurt to type, to pick up a pen.

The record was on its infinite end now, the song over and the needle softly scratching the edge.

"You don't understand," was all I could say.

She had the audacity to scoff at me. "The biggest middle finger you could ever throw up is to just keep going, you know."

"So eloquent."

She gave me an exaggerated shrug. "Pot, kettle. Kettle, pot. Nice to meet you. We should drink sometime."

I grunted, throwing the covers off of me and walking into the bathroom. I splashed cold water onto my face and gripped the sides of the sink, feeling the porcelain soothe my skin. My chest was constricting, a hundred vines tightening around my torso and slithering around each appendage until every muscle felt stiff. My breath caught in my throat—short gasps, then hiccuping ones—and it wasn't until I was shaking that Dee came in. She rested her hand on my back and made gentle circles.

"I can't," I managed to get out in a whisper. The water was collecting on the counter now, pooling with my leftover make-up from the day before in small puddles of cream watercolor.

"Yeah, babe, you can. It may not seem like it now, but you can. You will."

"How could you *possibly* even know?" I asked, my voice muffled in my hands. I tried to fight my fingertips from picking at the skin surrounding the nail beds. The sensation of blood collecting in the corners made me both wince and sigh with relief.

"Because I really don't have the energy to go through this every single day, for the love of Hades," she joked. "So, honestly, just do it for *me*."

A small laugh managed to escape between the shaky gasps of air. For a moment, I had been fighting to remember where I last put my inhaler, but the sharp exhale of breath made my chest relax ever so slightly. "I hate you so much."

"No, you don't. Nice try, though. Now, get dressed already—worlds to create and conquer!" She slapped my butt and left me alone to stare at my red face in the mirror. The thought of cracking open the laptop again made my stomach churn. The sentences, printed vines made up of sans serif letters, were still encircling me but had loosened their grip, forever taunting, forever calling—*make us grow*. I heard Dee fiddling with the laptop, then the record player, then her footsteps as she clomped her way to the kitchen to find any sort of sustenance. She would ultimately find herself disappointed. My breathing returned somewhat back to normal. The walls, feeling as if they could touch me if I only turned mere inches, seemed to finally give me space.

There were days when they collapsed on me, burying me in the damage.

One wreckage on top of another.

My phone began pinging, reminding me it was past the protective tunnel of the "do not disturb" window and well into the afternoon in the UK. Our group, half of us here in the states, half overseas, was continuing the collective bashing of our former leader to cope with the scars left behind. We saw everything in fire, tasted only bitterness. We were no longer about writing; we were about healing, even if the laughter was still tinged in misery. When the pings came through in a consistent stream, I grabbed the phone and read. I typed out a couple of comments and laughing emojis with one hand, the other clutching a bottle of pills I hadn't realized I grabbed; the ones reserved for a rescue, not a hospital room. *Just take one.* This, I knew, wouldn't heal the parts of me which were breaking. It was that first layer of thin epidermis over an open wound, a fragile thing struggling to turn the wound whole again but still an open window to the damage beneath. I told them I laughed out loud while tears clouded their comforting words.

Before I could get the cap open, Dee's hand grabbed the bottle and replaced it with a mug of coffee. It was a gift from a friend, a mock-up cover of my book if a publisher had printed it, the small bird on the logo stretching about in the center of the blue ribbon and clean font. I glared at Dee, though thankful for the gesture. "Rubbing it in is not helping the situation."

She feigned shock, a hand coming up to her mouth. "I would *never*."

"Yes, you would."

The hand dropped, all pretension out the window. "Okay, yes, I would."

I took a sip, never removing my gaze from her. She had her headphones on, one just slightly off her ear so she could hear me. "What are you listening to?"

She smiled, a devilish thing. I shouldn't have asked. "Inspiration for the sequel." She took the headphones off and tried to get them on my head. I pushed her hands away, leaving her in a huff. A plume of smoke seemed to erupt in her pupils.

"Just *listen*." I shook my head and ducked beneath the bridge of her arm, leaving the phone on the bed. With a shaking hand, I checked the baby monitor. I looked at my daughter, bundled tightly in her bassinet, and it gave me more warmth than the coffee in my hand. It was a reprieve.

I felt Dee's chin rest on my shoulder. Her voice was a mumble, her chin massaging my shoulder as she talked. "Do it for her, then."

"You're relentless."

"I mean, it's kind of your fault, though."

I let out a sigh, my eyes drifting from the monitor back to the laptop. The background, a photo of hydrangeas I snapped in Kilkenney, Ireland, settled a bit of the nerve in my stomach. It reminded me of stories that were real.

"Fine," I whispered. I felt the headphones gracefully come over my head. I heard the music start and felt the coffee hit my tongue, and I closed my eyes until the song's notes played out and the tears meant something else entirely.

•

Spring slowly and unbearably turned into summer. Redbuds and cottonwoods changed from their budding colors into their respective shades of green. Dee hated the season and made her complaints loud and clear, obnoxiously so. I didn't know who was the bigger child between her and my infant.

The world kept turning, love was plentiful, but the pages stayed empty.

The laptop collected dust.

It rained, and ideas came like fog, clouding over all of my thinking but dissipating just as fast.

Dee left for long periods at a time. Even she hated the blank space. I was starting to forget the tone of her voice.

When the leaves began to turn, Dee's mood improved.

She was rejuvenated and began to take me on again. I had missed her, though I'd never tell her as much. There was a day when she brought in a large maple leaf the color of burnt caramel and gave it to my daughter to play with (of which I immediately took away before she consumed), a day when she played nothing but opera and claimed it was "the epitome of good death," a day when she begged and begged until I finally gave in and made some home-made soup, and one when she sat next to me all day with her arms crossed and headphones on, bobbing her head to music and waiting for me to just ask.

I stood my ground. She stood hers.

Meanwhile, the phone pings died down to an occasional chime, as frequent as my inspiration.

•

When most of the life around us was still and asleep and the winter winds were blowing through, I awoke from a dream. It was an idea so vivid it clutched me by the arms, leaving phantom fingernail marks, whispering *don't you let me go*. I threw the covers off and began the long walk to my laptop with trepidation. I could see the charging light like a beacon, yet it froze me to the spot. It was cold in the room, despite the heater blowing through the vents. My thick socks now felt like concrete. I flexed my fingers, feeling my breath shallow and fill up, the never-ending tide within rocking me back and forth.

For a moment, I thought of those pills in the bathroom, their bitter coating, the comfort seeping over all of the fear. The fear to do this all over again.

Breathe.

"Here are your final royalties."

Breathe.

"Do you wish to take down this book listing?"

Breathe.

"Want to save your changes to this document?" Don't save.

Breathe.

"You can. And you will."

Breathe.

My feet moved, then my hands; my shaking fingers

grasped the back of the chair before pulling it out from under the desk. I opened the laptop. The screen was too bright, a full moon in the darkness, but I opened up a new document anyway.

"Fuck yes, you will," Dee muttered, her presence suddenly behind me. I jumped in my chair.

"*Carajo*, do you mind?"

"Listen, I've been waiting too damn long for this moment. Do *you* mind?"

"You're going to ruin this if you don't shut up and let me get this down."

She lifted her hands in surrender, a hint of a smile on her face. She walked over to the window, peeking behind the curtain. "It's almost dawn. A new day."

My fingers weren't moving, not yet. They hovered over the keys, wavering, unsure of the action. It was a piano, the music promising and haunting, echoing in the far reaches of my brain. I had spent so long with Mozart and Beethoven and pretending my compositions were a fraction of what theirs could be that I had forgotten what it meant to simply *play*. Fingertips finally met plastic and pressed down. Muscles and joints stretched like wakening yawns.

"Chapter One"
Enter-Enter
Tab

This is where it starts again. My phone dimly woke up its screen, signaling a message. I pulled it up in my browser instead. Whispers, after their seasonal hiatus, had sparked another fire of conversation, this time a phoenix of positivity.

"*When are we seeing Dee again?*" one of them asked me. "*That book needs to be out in the world.*"

"*Yeah, where's the sequel?*"

I smiled and felt Dee sit next to me on the floor. She stretched her legs out in front of her and leaned back on her elbows, sunglasses on her face like she's on a beach instead of a curtained room at night. She looked up at me and wiggled her eyebrows up past the line of the glasses. Death herself was unforgivingly casual, and I would never have it any other way. "Give the people what they want, is what I say."

I messaged back a "thanks" with a smiley face, this time genuine, this time without the dread of something else waiting for me. "One day, soon."

It's enough for now.

I looked back at the document and thought of this new world.

"They won't be as good as me, you know," Dee joked.

I laughed as I typed. *I was typing again.* "No, they'll be better."

She let out a gasp, pushing the glasses on top of her head and sitting up. "You take that back."

I stopped, swiveling in the chair and looking at her. "You never forget your first, though."

Her eyes narrowed at me, her gaze briefly turning to my screen. A flicker of a smile turned the corner of her lips upward. "No, I suppose not."

"Dee?"

"Yeah?" Her attention was back at me. Her fingers began fiddling with the watch pendant around her neck. A soft blue glow emitted from it, a makeshift heart. I sniffed back the tears clouding up my eyes. "Oh, don't you dare," she warned.

"Thank you, for everything."

She was practically frozen to the floor. The only noticeable movement was her tongue pushing against her cheek and her nostrils flaring. She managed to take a shuddering breath before finally breaking. She pushed the sunglasses back down on her face and pulled on the lapels of her leather jacket to straighten them. "Hades, you're *such* an asshole."

"I love you, too." I turned around and resumed typing, the weight of the keys underneath my fingers feeling more and more natural again.

"Hey," she said. Only her voice remained. The room was empty, save for my sleeping husband and snoring cat. At the same time she spoke, another message came through. *"We got you."*

"Yeah?" I asked Dee.

In my head, I could hear Bohemian Rhapsody in the

background, feel her rocking out on the bed, sense her warmth filling every corner of the space. "I will not let you go."

CLARE PROCTOR

POETRY

CLARE PROCTOR (b. 1980) was born and raised in a small village in Perthshire, Scotland. Stories were a central passion in her childhood, and her studies of Literature at University, along with travel, inspired Clare to become a writer. While working for her BA in English and American Literature, Clare co-edited the university literary magazine, *Logos*. Through studying for an MA in Modern Poetry, Clare became interested in poetry's political potential, focusing her research on Bob Perelman and the L=A=N=G=U=A=G=E poets. It was during this time that Clare had her first poem published in *French Literary Review*.

Becoming an English teacher enabled Clare to share her love of Literature with young people and facilitate creative writing in others. After moving to Cumbria, she began to take her own writing more seriously. The accountability and feedback opportunities provided through writing groups led to an increase in submissions made. Over the years, Clare was published in the magazines *Shooter*, *The North*, *A3 Review*, and *Finished Creatures* and in anthologies by The Frogmore Press, Yaffle Press and the Handstand Press Anthology of New Cumbrian Writing—*This Place I Know*. She came second place in the Canterbury Festival competition 2018 and won the Cumbrian Poet's Prize in the Poem and a Pint Competition in 2019.

Clare regularly performs in the Cumbrian Open Mic where Ann Grant, host of Kendal's monthly Verbalise says of Clare's work—"It's always a pleasure to read a Clare Proctor poem, her tender and authentic voice provides a feast for the senses. Her poems are touching, thoughtful and leave you wanting more."

On Falling In Love With Poets

I have fallen in love with poets,
with the spaces they hold within them
like underground caves. I want to be
lowered into those caves with a head-torch,
reach my hands out to the walls,
scarred with their stories. I want to fall
into their voices, when they do not hesitate,
but resonate, like the deep note
of the viola. I love the idea
of falling in love with poets, and in love
with all that they have loved;
with their moments of climax,
with their late-night tears,
with their misspoken words that slip
from their lips when angry or drunk or tired.
I want to fall for their suffering,
dip into it like a well,
wash in its dark water.
I want to feel their pain, like splinters
stuck in the skin of my fingers.
I have fallen in love with the word—poet—
how the two soft syllables shape my mouth.

A Stolen Thing

If this word is a stolen thing,
I want to be the eyes
that glanced around, checking for security;
I want to be the fingers
that swiped it from its shelf;
I want to be the legs that turned
as other words were thrown;
I want to be the back that felt them batter;
I want to be the running, the breathing,
the picking up of pace.

This word turns me into a runaway,
searching for a cave, cold and still,
where the echo of this word
can return and return
to beat its restless syllables
against the walls.

GRETCHEN KELLY

Keep Going

NON-FICTION

GRETCHEN KELLY was born in North Carolina in 1973, raised by a single mom who sang feminist anthems instead of lullabies and encouraged free thinking. She swore she'd leave one day and unabashedly be her true self. In many ways, the only truth was in the words that spilled out of her. In college, she dabbled in writing for the school newspaper, but felt confined by the structure.

It wasn't until after she had a family of her own that she began writing again. One of her first syndicated articles detailed how she got through her wedding day only ten days after her brother died from cancer. This article would be the jumping point for her memoir work-in-progress about coming of age in the 80s and 90s and the impact of her brother's life and death.

When an article about everyday sexism and the toll it takes on girls and women went viral, she found her words resonating with women all over the world. Promoted in multiple outlets and published in six different languages, her article was changing the conversation on sexism. She was listed in *Huffington Post's* "2015 Most Buzzworthy Blogs." Later, she took on a role as a featured writer for the *Good Men Project* and led their *Stop Sexism* podcast and social interest group. She's a contributing writer to "The Mom's Guide to Becoming Socially Active and Politically Engaged" in the *Lose the Cape* book series, and in "I Just Want to Hang Out With You" via the *New York Times* best selling "I Just Want to Pee Alone" series. Gretchen Kelly still lives in the South, but has embraced the beauty and soul that resides among the darker past, and through her writing has found that long silenced voice.

He made his fingers dance in front of him. With one eyebrow raised, he looked at me as if asking a question and answering it at the same time.

"What? Oh." Recognition set in. Typing. He was mimicking rapid typing.

Crossing and uncrossing my legs, I shifted irritably. Yes, writing is what I needed to do. I already knew I needed to find the time and motivation to write again. In fact, I'd said as much, many times over the years in his office. But it wasn't the solution to everything. The idea that anxiety and grief and fear could be resolved by a simple act was insulting. He was my therapist, not my writing coach. Maybe he'd known me too long and become too comfortable with my easy nature. Maybe the smile I hid behind made him think I was a puzzle solved without effort.

But I couldn't shake the fact that there was probably some truth to what he'd said.

I don't know when I decided I was a writer. Or if I even decided. Maybe it had always been there, like background music I didn't recognize. Perhaps it was born of necessity—a need to process my life, a catharsis via words. Or was it a lack of talent in other arts? Music would surely have been my life if I'd possessed any sense of rhythm or tone. Lyrics and melody had always spoken to me. Was I a writer by default? All I know is that in the third grade, my inner-writer was coaxed out of hiding.

Her name was Ms. Abraham. She was loud. Brash. She could cut you with a look or smile at you as if you were her favorite. Her classroom crackled with energy. Her rules were clear: *No disrespect. No gum chewing.* That was it. She would remind us by pointing to them with her long yardstick, popping her own gum for emphasis. I was in awe of her contradictions. The message was clear—she was the teacher, and she could do as she pleased. We only had to follow two simple rules and we would do *just fiiiine*. She always drew that word out. The first time she said it, the students exchanged glances of uncertainty. Fine didn't sound fine when she said it like that.

There was an intimacy to her classroom that was different from the others—less formal, less authoritarian, more laughter.

162

She had a casual nature. She made up nicknames for her students and only called us by our real names if we were in trouble. A raucous class didn't phase her, as long as we didn't take it too far. I sometimes felt sorry for the other third grade students who had uptight teachers. Teachers who didn't crack jokes or sing in the middle of a lesson. Who didn't pause in writing on the blackboard to pull up their long skirt and inch their pantyhose up their leg, leaving the class in giggles. No, their teachers expected strict obedience and silence . . . and also no gum chewing.

You didn't ask questions in Ms. Abraham's class without carefully considering them. So when she showed up with a hand truck loaded up with two large boxes, none of us said a word. We knew eventually she'd tell us what was in the boxes. After she smoothed her skirt and patted her hair, she addressed us.

"Today, y'all are gonna learn to write."

She reached into the box, pulled out a handful of magazines, and dropped them on the table with a loud thud. Ms. Abraham didn't do anything quietly; everything was punctuated with a clap, a laugh, or a stomping of her knee-high boots. This was no different.

The assignment was to find a photo in one of the magazines and write a story around it. That was it. There were no rules other than "do your best," which we'd already learned fell under the "no disrespect" commandment. Hands shot in the air, hungry for more guidance and direction. She waved us away.

"Nope. Figure it out. Just write. That's it."

We looked around as if seeking answers from each other.

"Well? Get to it."

I wrestled with the assignment. The pleaser in me wanted to know how to do this right. I craved her approval and wanted to make her proud. How could I do this if I didn't know what she was looking for? I grabbed my paper and pencil and approached her desk. She didn't even look up from her grade book as she twirled her finger at me.

"Turn yourself around and sit back down, Ms. Thing. You aren't getting any more from me."

My face burned hot from her swift refusal. I slid my pencil

back and forth in the groove at the top of the desk, paralyzed by the freedom she'd granted. While the other students were scribbling and erasing with some kind of internal direction, I sat fighting tears. The freedom to say and do anything unnerved me. I craved clearly marked lanes instead of a wide open road. Left to my own inner compass, I felt lost.

I don't remember what I wrote about. Eventually, I filled the page with words—half-hearted, lackluster words. Words that would not impress anyone, let alone Ms. Abraham. There were no grades on these assignments—just feedback. *You can do MUCH better* was scrawled in red across the page. And below that, in a softer script, *Keep going.* Her disappointment was expected, but the encouragement wasn't. I felt something akin to . . . support? Hope? Whatever it was, it made me want to write again and show her she wasn't wrong.

The writing assignment continued weekly. Eventually, I got into the flow and embraced the freedom. The feedback became more positive, always pushing me to go further.

This is good, but what else can you say about it? Keep going.

Keep going. That fed me. The nourishment my tepid writer craved. *Keep going* meant what I said had value, that it wasn't silly or stupid. That the carefully cultivated words and behavior I presented to the world were not necessary. Something in me awoke that year in Ms. Abraham's class, a freedom to express myself I didn't feel anywhere else. Writing became my escape. The outside world ceased to exist when I was writing. It was my refuge.

Years passed. College. Marriage. Loss. Children. Life. All of it took precedence over writing.

Writing became a distant goal, a "one day" wistful refrain. Being a writer had been part of my identity since the third grade, but with nothing published since my college newsletter, I felt like a fraud claiming it.

Which is how I found myself squirming in my therapist's office. Life had dealt its blows, as it does. My brother was diagnosed with stage-four cancer a month after I got engaged. He died ten days before my wedding. My first child was born a year after he died. The nexus of his death was the thing that had most affected me but also the thing I'd allowed life to obscure. Marriage, children . . . busyness were the blinders I wore. I tricked myself into thinking he was just away on a long trip. That one day, he'd walk through the door, and I'd hug him and tell him how much I'd missed him before chastising him for being gone for so long. We'd laugh and resort to our teasing banter.

But that was not going to happen. I'd sat by his side when he took his last, labored breaths. I'd watched them lower him into the ground. And I was doing everything in my limited power to ignore those memories and pretend like it was all a bad dream. Writing was too dangerous. Writing was truth, and I was too scared to face it. So, I denied myself my vital outlet. I pushed my voice and my need to write into the deeper recesses of my mind, using the role of wife and mother as a scapegoat for abandoning it. I was annoyed that my therapist thought the solution to what ailed me lay in pursuing my passion. Irritated because it scared me. It's terrifying to try the thing you love. The thing that you think about daily. The thing that means so much that to do it and fail would be so painful you're not sure you could come back and try again. The thing you talk yourself out of every time you think you might attempt it. The thing that doesn't let you hide from the truth.

The thing you've loved since third grade.

He was right. I needed to write. Putting it off was leaving a hole in me that anxiety was residing in. But actually doing it felt . . . terrifying. Overwhelming. Paralyzing. I felt like I was right back in that classroom, tears stinging my eyes, not knowing how to begin to write. So I did what I do best: I put it out of my mind, telling myself that I would feel a nudge when the time was right. My nudge came while I was driving one afternoon—alone, windows rolled down and music turned up. The song shifted, and slow streams of music filled the car, begging me to listen. The song, the winding road I was driving- it was as if they were con-spiring to reach me. I passed my turn and kept driving. I needed to wander; I needed to absorb the moment. The languishing wail wrapped in wistful lyrics, it was breathtaking. It was the kind of art that opens up part of you that you thought you'd buried. Art that makes you want to create art. I was transported by the slow melody, the words draped in sepia. I was back in the third grade, running through neighbors' backyards or in my bedroom, lying on the floor with my headphones on. I was back in the woods lounging in a makeshift fort, telling stories with my friends and making plans for mischief. As I listened to the poetry playing out in a haunting melody, I felt something awaken and break through the noise of life, motherhood, marriage, grocery lists, and to-dos. Tears spilled over, and I felt relief, urgency, and direction. In that moment, a song I'd heard dozens of times before opened up a part of me that I had long since filed away.

I needed words to fill my life again. I needed to play with them, to bounce them around and weigh their worth. I was ready for the sport, clumsy and wooden, but ready. I took the voice that had accompanied me all those years and put it on paper. I wrote the chapters I'd been composing in my head for years. I started publishing my words for an audience for the first time since college. I had forgotten the excruciating tediousness that comes between the stops and starts. I became reacquainted with the particular kind of torture that is baring your soul on the page.

I'll never get used to writing. It will always make me question my worth; it will always vex me. I will always marvel at the effortlessness that appears without warning, then fades just as quickly. And I will chase that feeling, that high no drug can touch—the purity of words flowing seamlessly, bumping up against the frustration of drought. Starting is the hardest part. But so is finishing. And the in-between. At the root of it all, what matters is that you keep pushing, keep giving voice to the words begging to be heard. The best critique and the highest compliment I've ever received is what sustains me when I feel like giving up. *Keep going.*

Acknowledgments

First and foremost, *Byline Legacies* would not exist were it not for the enthusiasm of the online writing community. You inspired the idea, supported us through our early stages, and continue to flood our notifications with so much love. You've allowed this book to be a truly collaborative project, as your generous feedback helped us shape the book into something we are so proud of. We are thankful for all of our Cardis! This book is for you, and we sincerely hope it is everything you could wish for.

From this very community came our brilliant, eagle-eye proof team. There are not enough words to express how much peace of mind and renewed focus Laurie Riihimaki, Bri Eberhart, and Andrew Robinette brought to the production of this book. Laurie, you care so much about the intention of each line, making us rethink our initial decisions in all the best ways. Bri, you are such a ray of sunshine on our stressful days, not to mention a comma commander! Andrew, you are a wonderful problem-solver, no matter the situation. Please know that you three have a permanent home at Cardigan.

To our sweet authors—you have been the best contributors we could have hoped for. You filled this book with incredible talent, words that fueled our emotions because they reminded us so much of ourselves. Your love for the craft pulsates off the pages, and we feel incredibly priviledged to present your narratives to the world. Lifting you up is our forever passion. We wanted to bring so much into your life, but it turned out the other way around. From emails with a bazillion exclamation marks to Facebook parties with tons of laughter to silly threads on Twitter, you embraced us like family. We will always feel a special connection to every one of you.

Lastly, we want to thank all the people in our life who invested hours of either listening to us talk nonstop about Cardigan or suffered hours of neglect while we poured ourselves into building this small press. To Jesse and Eric—our mental and emotional ability to create this would have suffered greatly without you to lean on.

Thank you for being our teammates and filling in the gaps. Jesse, thank you for giving us a concept for the cover that we were excited about, and Eric, thank you for digitalizing the art! Cardigan is our baby, and you graciously gave us the space to raise it right. Thank you for understanding our passion and encouraging us to shine. We love you.

Contributor Media

Aaron Sandberg
Instagram: @aarondsandberg

Abasiama Udom
SmashWords: Abasiama Udom

Alessandor Earnest
Twitter: @TheImpOfEditing
Instagram: @TheImpOfEditing
Site: www.theimportanceofediting.com

Allene Nichols
Blog: www.allenen.wordpress.com/author/allenen/

Anisha Kaul
Twitter: @anishakaul9
Site: www.anishakaul9.wixsite.com/poet/

Carol Beth Anderson
Twitter: @CBethAnderson
Instagram: @cbethanderson
Facebook: @carolbethanderson
BookBub: @carolbethanderson
Books listed on Goodreads!

Carol Casey
Facebook: @ccaseypoetry
Twitter: @ccasey_carol
Site: www.learnforlifepotential.com/home-2/poetry/

Carson Sandell
Site: www.carsonsandell.com

Christiana Doucette
Twitter: @doucette515
Instagram: @doucette515
Clare Proctor
Twitter: @almostasif

Coral Rivera
Twitter: @coralrivwrites
Instagram: @coralriverawrites
WattPad: @theladyreva
Site: www.coralrivera.com

Dale Parnell
Facebook: @shortfictionauthor

Daniel Hinds
Twitter: @DanielGHinds

David Jesson
Twitter: @BreakerofThings
Site: www.fictioncanbefun.wordpress.com

Dee Richards
Twitter: @DeeRichardsSD
Blog: www.deerichardswrites.medium.com

Deryck N. Robertson
Twitter: @canoe_ideas
Site: www.canoeideas.wordpress.com

Eden Campbell
Twitter: @authoredenc

Elizabeth Bates
Twitter: @ElizabethKBates
Site: www.elizabethkatebates.wixsite.com/writer

Gretchen Kelly
Twitter: @gkelly73
Facebook: @driftingthrough
Medium: @gretchenkellywrites

Guitar Hanna
Twitter: @guitarhanna
Site: www.guitarhanna.com

Jane Schapiro
Facebook: @jane.schapiro.9
Site: www.janeschapiro.com

Jenn Jarrett
Twitter: @JennTJarrett

Jessica Sarlin
Twitter: @JessSarlin
Instagram: @JessSarlin

Jonathan Petley
Twitter: @spacedoxie
Instagram: @spacedoxie
Site: www.jonathanpetley.com

Kate Kenzie
Twitter: @kakenzie101
Instagram: @kakenzie101
Site: www.katekenzie.com

Kelly Esparza
Twitter: @Kelly_Esparza7
Site: www.kellyesparza.wordpress.com

L. Dacre Tynan
Twitter: @Elbow_Jumper
Blog: www.ldtynan.home.blog

Lynn Katz
Site: www.lynnkatzauthor.com

Margarita Baressi
Twitter: @Barresi_Writes
Site: www.margaritabarresi.com

Mark Tulin
Site: www.crowonthewire.com

Marco Santomenna
Twitter: @author_mds

Michael Pudney
Site: www.michaelpudney.com

Michelle Tang
Twitter: @a_girl_Michelle

R. Tim Morris
Twitter: @RyMo89
Site: www.rtimmorris.com/shop/

Shane Schick
Twitter: @shaneschick

Sher Ting
Twitter: @shertt
Site: www.downintheholocene.wordpress.com

Toni Wall
Twitter: @justaddpages
Instagram: @justaddpages
Facebook: @ToniWallWrites

Valerie Hunter
Instagram: @somanystories_solittletime

About the editors

JAIME DILL

Jaime Dill is a North Carolinian soul who grew up on a healthy mix of classics, poetry, and young adult fiction. She uses her broad editorial skill by helping other writers as a freelance editor and book coach through her own company, Polish & Pitch, established in 2018. Jaime is most appreciative of editing commercial fiction because it has allowed her to integrate her love of genre fiction with the technical skill gained during her studies as a Creative Writing student. "The line between literary and genre is one many people don't like to toe, but crossing easily between the two allows imagination and skill to mingle and learn from each other without risk of cancelling each other out."

Visit www.linktr.ee/jaime_dill for links to Jaime's writing, editorial services, and media.

LIZZIE THORNTON

Lizzie Thornton of Lady Lizzie Editing is a gifted book coach, developmental editor, and line editor, who enjoys working with a multitude of genres and characters but specializes in books that include strong female-identifying characters. Growing up in a transient military family, the world of literature was her solace. While getting her Bachelor's at the University of South Carolina, she discovered she thrived in the workshop-style classes. From this grew a love for reading works-in-progress and helping shape creative ideas into something brilliant. "When I read an author's story that they've entrusted to me, I am dedicated and bound to amplifying their words. My purpose is not to change their art, but to help better position it in a gallery so more people can be swept away by it."

Visit www.linktr.ee/iamladylizzie for links to Lizzie's latest article, editorial services, and media.

CPSIA information can be obtained
at www.ICGtesting.com
Printed in the USA
LVHW090132140921
697745LV00001B/6